HUBERT J. KARREMAN, V.M.D.

90+ REAL-WORLD CASES

THE

BARN GUIDE

(to) *Treating Dairy Cows Naturally*

PRACTICAL ORGANIC COW CARE FOR FARMERS

Acres U.S.A. / Austin, Texas

The Barn Guide to Treating Dairy Cows Naturally

Acres U.S.A. // P.O. Box 91299 // Austin, Texas 78709 U.S.A.

(512) 892-4400 // fax (512) 892-4448 // info@acresusa.com // www.acresusa.com

Printed in the United States of America

Publisher's Cataloging-in-Publication

Karreman, Hubert, J. 1962-
The barn guide to treating dairy cows naturally / Hubert J. Karreman.
Austin, TX, ACRES U.S.A., 2011
192 pp., 25 cm.
Includes Index
ISBN 978-1-60173-023-7 (trade)

1. Dairy cattle — Diseases — Naturopathic treatment. 2. Dairy Cattle — Diseases — Prevention. 3. Dairy farms — Management. 4. Holistic veterinary medicine — United States. I. Karreman, Hubert, 1962- II. Title.

SF961.K37 2011   636.2089

Trademark Acknowledgements

Betadine™ is a registered trademark of Purdue Pharma. Biocel CBT™, Ecto-Phyte™ are registered trademarks of Agri-Dynamics. Bovi-Sera™ is a registered trademark of Colorado Serum Company. Endovac-Bovi™ is a registered trademark of Immvac. Immunoboost™ is a registered trademark of Bioniche Animal Health. J-5™, Thera-Bloat™ are registered trademarks of Pfizer. J-Vac™ is a registered trademark of Merial. MuSe™ is a registered trademark of Intervet. Get Well™, Heat Seek™, Phyto-Gest™, Phyto-Mast™, Phyto-Biotic™, Plasma Gold™ are registered trademarks of Penn Dutch Cow Care. Poly Serum™ is a registered trademark of Novartis. Portasol™ is a registered trademark of Oglesby & Butler. Royal™ Uterine Capsules is a registered trademark of Van Beek Natural Science. RumenAider®, Pyck-Me-Up™, Generator™ Elite, Pecti-Cap™, Cal-D Cap™ are registered trademarks of Bio-Vet. Utresept™ is a registered trademark of Integrated Bio Systems. CharCal™ and "0" 1:2 Special are registered trademarks of Midwestern Bio-Ag.

Acknowledgements

This book would not have been possible without the help of some very important people. I thank the great team at Acres U.S.A. who helped put this book together — Anne Van Nest, Bryan Kight and Fred Walters. Anne, my editor, has been wonderful in quickly communicating questions or changes that were needed, sifting through the rough original text and organizing it into a user-friendly manual. Special thanks to Bryan, art director for staring at some rather unpleasant medical pictures of cow conditions while he decided where to place them. And Fred, who sits at the helm of Acres U.S.A., is simply a very pleasant person to chat with about the world and especially those events in the agricultural realm. With his wife Kathy and his brother Chris also involved, Fred continues the tradition of Acres U.S.A. being a true family business.

Closer to home, I want to thank my wife Becky and our daughter Emily. They have had to deal with me being so immersed as a veterinarian in organics for so many years now — times when I would simply "not be there" because a cow needed help or someone was calling with a question about organic livestock and needing an answer right away. Becky did a great job of proofreading the final draft of the book and I thank her for many common sense changes that were needed. She always comes up with very useful suggestions, whether it is for work or family matters. And special thanks to Emily for helping come up with the title of this book — as well as allowing me to use her special red pen as I proof read the draft copy.

Additionally, thanks to Dave Harnish of DDL Distributors in East Earl, Pennsylvania. He had great information for some of the products listed for the digestive cases. I first met Dave as his dairy vet in the mid-1990s. He is always helpful — if you are broken down along the side of the road, you can only hope that Dave will be driving by because he will stop and help anybody.

. . . .

Photos Note: All photos, except those noted here were taken by the author. Front cover of Dr. Karreman with "Loretta" and back cover photos with "Sonia" were taken by Edie Griffiths, Seven Star Farm, Kimberton, PA. Photos of hoof surgery on pages 56 and 141 were taken by Megan McBride.

. . . .

Disclaimer: The contents of this book represent views on traditional and contemporary treatments and compile clinically useful information but are not intended or offered to supplant the advice or service of a trained professional veterinarian that has an established veterinary-client-patient-realtionship.

🐄 Dedication

This book is dedicated to all the dairy farmers I have come to know — locally in my home area of Lancaster County, Pennsylvania and across the United States into Canada (way up to Fort Assiniboine, Alberta), all the way to South Korea . . . and of course in my "other" country — Holland.

I sincerely hope that this book is useful to you. I have learned from all of the insights that you and your cows have given me and can only hope that I have been of help to you along the way.

Biodiversity includes breed diversity on some farms.

"Lady" — 18-years old at the time of this photograph.

Typical farm in Lancaster County, Pennsylvania.

Nice looking Jersey bull — never to trust!

Cows — good looking and where they should be.

Excellent bedding and beautiful clean cows.

🐄 Introduction from Hubert Karreman, V.M.D.

In my first book, *Treating Dairy Cows Naturally* (Acres U.S.A., 2007), I was striving to give the reader a very full and comprehensive picture of organic dairy health care and alternative veterinary medicine. In the treatments section I tried to be all-inclusive and in doing so may have given *too* many choices from which to select.

Additionally, I realized that when listing topics by disease name (pneumonia, twisted stomach, etc.), people may not necessarily know how to diagnose certain conditions and therefore not feel secure about choosing treatments. This book deals with this issue and strives to be very basic in its approach — presenting a thorough examination of an animal in the barn and then primarily listing symptoms with pictures that the farmer can see, offering possible conclusions, and then giving a small set of treatments.

While this book has many pictures, not all conditions can be photographed nor have I encountered all conditions that farmers may see. However, I have seen the vast majority of types of cases and hopefully I'll be able to effectively cover about 100 common and not-so-common problems. The treatments are ones I have found to work consistently well while in "the trenches" with organic cows for many years.

This book is meant to be very practical and instantly usable in the barn. It is a "boiled down" account of cases I have seen and how I have approached such cases over 15 years in practice. The fundamentals of organic and holistic thinking about livestock are presented first. This is to help you approach real-life situations more effectively in the barn and around the farm. Always remember that natural treatments work best if based on a holistic preventive foundation.

ORGANIC LIVESTOCK FUNDAMENTALS

Ideally, a farm should be biologically alive and as self-sufficient as possible. Being self-sufficient means that most of your crops are home grown and you rely on your own ingenuity to get things done rather than relying on outside inputs and custom work done by others. Self-sufficiency usually means increased profitability, as well as fewer out-of-pocket costs. Self-sufficiency works best when there is an optimal amount of livestock on a farm in relation to the arable and grazing land base. A rough estimate is that it takes about three acres per cow (including young stock) to have enough land to be fully self-sufficient.

It is of utmost importance that the soils be biologically active and physically aerated with good water movement throughout the soil profile, not just a medium to which fertilizers are applied. This concept is central to the sustainable and organic philosophy. Healthy soils are best reflected when the animals are healthiest from grazing well-managed pastures during the growing season. Additionally, when there is a balance of livestock and land base, there will probably be little to no pollution leaving the farm.

The awareness of the farmer for the animals under their care and how they are directly tied to the landscape will hopefully stimulate a sense of wonder and awe about how all life on the farm is interconnected. It is on farms with conscientious farmers that the food produced will likely be found to be rich in nutrients — thus being more energetic and supplying of vitality to all life that is dependent on the farm, whether it be people, wildlife, birds, frogs, fish and insects. It is then that the local community best benefits from such a farm in its surroundings. Farms like this are a true jewel in the local landscape.

WITHIN ORGANIC SYSTEMS

As a field veterinarian I learned to avoid guaranteeing things when considering the complexities and fragilities associated with biological life. However, I can state with near certainty that a farmer who farms more in line with mother nature will have dramatically fewer problems. With this in mind, it will become obvious that exerting absolute control over all aspects of the farm is simply absurd. You really need to release the concept of having absolute control over the farm. If this is a difficult concept to accept, biological and organic farming may not be a good option to pursue. Moreover, maximizing production is *not* the goal of organics. While a reasonable level of production can be achieved, trying to achieve recognition for high production will leave you very frustrated. And finally, prevention is especially critical in organics.

Relying on synthetic inputs or pharmaceutical crutches is simply not feasible with organic regulations — nor is it wise in the long run. The reliance upon silver bullets or simply replacing conventional inputs with organically acceptable inputs (input substitution) is contrary to biological agriculture and should be unlearned as early as possible. Therefore, good planning and the use of a multi-prong approach to both prevention and treatment will be very helpful. By not relying on chemicals and drugs, you get to rely more on your own vision, intellect and fortitude to steer your farm.

FORMULA FOR HEALTHY ORGANIC LIVESTOCK

Many in organic livestock agriculture subscribe to and promote the concept: healthy soils = healthy crops = healthy animals. This simple concept is catchy and applies best to animals that are outside grazing managed pasture land. However, I find the statement to be overly simplistic and somewhat misleading to beginning organic farmers. Why? Because there are usually many steps between what is in the ground to the time the feed is fed out to the animals.

Beginning holistic farmers need encouragement within realistic parameters. From my experience as a farm veterinarian, I know what factors create the healthiest animals. The following statement encompasses the entire year, including wintertime housing and feeding, which can be for half the year in many northern dairy climates.

DRY BEDDING

+ FRESH AIR

+ SUNSHINE

+ WELL-MANAGED PASTURES

+ HIGH FORAGE RATIONS

= HEALTHY ANIMALS

BODY CONDITION

Body condition will generally change during each stage of milk production. The more milk a cow makes, the leaner and skinnier she will become. However, after peak milk (after 90 days in milk), body condition should start to return. If not, the cow will likely not cycle normally to become pregnant again in a timely fashion. That said, grazing cattle tend to be sleek athletes due to their exercising everyday. They should have glossy coats and well-defined muscles, be bright and alert, and most importantly — have good rumen fill.

Herds of cows that are chronically skinny are likely to be modern Holsteins or Jerseys as they have a relatively higher demand for energy inputs (grain). If a person wants to feed a low grain diet due to high organic grain pricing or due to direct customers wanting milk from only grassfed cows, it would be wise to consider using the minor breeds (Milking Shorthorn, Lineback, Dutch Belted, Normande, etc.) or mixed breeds. These other breeds are usually more efficient in feed intake as reflected by better body condition throughout the lactation.

GENERAL RATION FOR ORGANIC HOLSTEINS PRODUCING ABOUT 60 LBS. (28 KG) OF MILK

Many of my clients in Lancaster County, Pennsylvania have predominantly Holstein cows although there are also some mixed breeds. Some herds are all mixed breeds and I like to think of them as "rainbow herds." While Jersey herds are not uncommon on grazing farms, Holsteins are still the dominant breed throughout the dairy world.

The following is a typical ration from my area here in Pennsylvania to feed grazing Holsteins so they maintain a reasonable body condition. First, of course, is to graze well-managed pastures during the grazing season. That is basic. However, if the pasture is too lush, most of the nutrient value of the pasture moves too quickly through the digestive tract and ends up splattering the general area. Try to graze paddocks between 10-14" (grass and alfalfa) and 7-8" for clover so as to obtain some fiber. Use BMR sorghum-sudangrass as an insurance policy to have green grazable material during the heat of summer. Cows like it. Also, feed as much grassy-mixed legume hay as they will consume — this is especially important prior to cattle grazing legume (clover/alfalfa) pastures for many days on end.

However, cows tend not to like dry hay during grazing season, yet they need to have it for effective fiber in the rumen. To entice them to eat it, pour molasses on it. The

CONCEPTS FOR TACKLING ILLNESS IN ORGANIC LIVESTOCK

There are *three critical concepts* that must be understood and embraced when considering natural treatments that are allowed for organic livestock. They are straightforward and pretty much self-explanatory.

DETECT MINOR CHANGES

You have to learn to see slight variations from normal in individual animals in regards to their routine behaviors of eating, milking, resting and walking. This is because you *must* jump on problems *early* when utilizing natural methods of treatments. You cannot let a problem go and simply hope for the best. I realize hope springs eternal for many farmers, as it should when living with ever changing weather patterns. But in living creatures, biological realities can quietly and sometimes quickly change into full-blown illness.

The whole basis of natural treatments is to stimulate and/or augment the animal's natural immune system, to rally and overcome challenges without relying on antibiotics and hormones. Of course a more natural living condition (*i.e.* grazing and high forage diets) will give a good baseline from which to start. Remember, the closer you can mimic mother nature in your animal's routine, the less problems you will have and the better chances of success without using antibiotics and hormones.

NATURAL TREATMENTS MAY BE LABOR INTENSIVE

Please realize that, unlike a quick shot of an antibiotic, most natural treatments involve more administrations of the treatment. This is because natural treatments tend to be more than a single "silver bullet." Just as prevention relies on a multi-prong approach, oftentimes the treatments do as well. Therefore, taking care of livestock in methods acceptable to organic production means that the farmer or herdsperson takes the extra time to investigate a problem and work with the animal for the best success.

NATURAL APPROACHES MAY TAKE LONGER TO SHOW RESULTS

Treatments that rely on stimulating or augmenting the animals' own immune defenses may take a bit longer than a quick antibiotic shot. But there are times when a correctly applied therapeutic biologic, can give an extremely quick response — often seen the same day. Additionally, an animal which is primarily helped by supportive and stimulating treatments will probably be stronger in the end than an animal which relies less on itself than upon a strong antibiotic.

molasses will not only sweeten it but also provides energy to help metabolize all the protein coming into the cow's system from the pasture. It takes energy to help convert the protein nitrogen to urea and then on to urine. If not provided in the ration, then energy will be drawn from the cow's reserves to do the biochemical transformations.

As far as grain feeding, a good rule of thumb is no more than one percent of body weight fed as grain in pounds in a day, but hopefully not fed as a two slug shot.

The next ingredient I like to see is usually controversial by true graziers but enjoyed by those organic farms that feed a little more conventionally — corn silage. Why corn silage? For two reasons, cows really like it and it maintains body condition really well. Additionally, it is a source of energy, which can reduce the need for purchased grains. While I do like corn silage in the diet of grazing cows, it shouldn't be fed more than 20-30 pounds per day. If you are really opposed to corn silage, ensiled brown midrib (BMR) sorghum-sudangrass has about the same energy content as corn silage if harvested properly. However, make sure it is baleage with its long fibrous leaves (*i.e.* don't chop it).

Some ideas for minerals: kelp (an excellent source of scores of minerals in a biologically available form), Midwestern Bio-Ag's "O" 1:2 Special (calcium carbonate, calcium sulphate, mono/dicalcium phosphate, monosodium phosphate, sulfate trace elements, vitamins A, D & E and added selenium), CharCal (an organic carbon-mineral complex of trace minerals with natural mined calcium and sulfur), salt, diatomaceous earth, humates and sodium bicarbonate — in the diet *and* as free choice.

Minor breeds such as Milking Shorthorns, Linebacks, Dutch Belted, Normandes or smaller versions of Holsteins such as the New Zealand Holstein or Jersey, and also the Finnish and Swedish Red-and-Whites will be easier to feed on low grain or no-grain diets as they seem to convert feed into body condition more efficiently. This may also be due to making less milk generally (with a higher percent of butterfat and protein).

Regardless of breed, every spring and early autumn I get at least a few calls from farmers who have severely *bloated cows* or even ones that have simply been found dead. *You can never have enough dry hay on a dairy farm*. I am constantly amazed how many farmers are almost adverse to dry hay these days. Yes, baleage is easier to produce but baleage does not always have enough *effective* fiber for a healthy rumen, especially during lush growth of pasture. Serious graziers having cows with clinical rumen acidosis during the early grazing season have proved this.

ABOUT ANTIBIOTICS

I am *not* philosophically opposed to antibiotics in all circumstances — I simply cannot reach for them as a first line treatment when treating organic dairy cows. And also remember that antibiotics still need a functioning immune system to be effective. The only function an antibiotic has is to kill bacteria (both bad and good) until the immune system can regain equilibrium and begin the recuperation process.

A therapeutic antibiotic certainly can be worth its weight in gold if used judiciously and not too late in the course of a disease. *It cannot be overstated that each and every case of infectious disease is different due to the individual animal's constitutional susceptibility or resistance to challenge.*

With stringent rules against antibiotics in U.S. organic livestock production, two questions immediately arise:

What are some reasonable alternative treatments that exist?

When is it appropriate to start an antibiotic in an organic setting?

Some reasonable alternative treatments include:

Biologics — medicines derived from living organisms, whether from the soil, plants or animals. These usually stimulate or augment the immune system. They are manufactured by purification processes and include colostrum whey products, botulism antitoxin, tetanus antitoxin, commercial antibodies for injection, and vaccines.

Botanicals — medicines derived from the plant kingdom. They have various effects on the physiology of an animal owing to a multitude of pharmacologically active compounds present. They are manufactured either as fluids or concentrated powders or dried crude herb. Available as tinctures, fluid extracts, extracts, teas, infusions, decoctions, etc.

Acupuncture — a medical system that takes into account the various paths of energy that flow throughout a living being (called meridians). Various neuro-humoral pathways have been shown to exist in association with the meridians. Points upon the meridians are stimulated by inserting needles into the area.

Homeopathy — medicines derived from mineral, plant or animal origin, or from disease discharges. These promote the vitality of the organism receiving the medicine. Depending upon the starting material, they are manufactured as powders or liquids which are then diluted and succussed to achieve the desired potency. Common homeopathic remedies show a potency of designation using the Roman numeral system which shows how many times the original material was diluted (the number in front of the letter) by the dilution factor (X = 1 in 10, C = 1 in 100, M = 1 in 1,000) *i.e.* 12X, 30C, 200C or 1M, etc.

Within the above four groups, there are practitioners that use subsets of these modalities depending on what they have found to be the most effective in their practice. For instance, practitioners of botanical medicine may use a single ingredient or they may use formulas (formulas are more common).

With acupuncture, some practitioners will use only dry needling whereas others may incorporate electro-acupuncture and aquapuncture (injection of vitamins at acupuncture points). Homeosinatry is the art of injecting liquid homeopathic remedies at acupuncture points and has been practiced since the late 1800s.

In homeopathy, some practitioners may routinely use and advocate very high potencies (primarily using only the essence of the starting material) whereas others may use low potencies (to use slight bits of the starting material) while others like myself have discovered the double benefit of using a specific remedy in multi-potency (combining low and high potencies).

Of course there are many other types of alternatives available, such as radionics, all with varying degrees of evidence for their effectiveness.

When is it appropriate to start an antibiotic in an organic setting?

Unfortunately there is no simple formula about when to start an antibiotic and it truly is on a case-by-case basis. However, over the years I have found that there are three types of situations that warrant the use of antibiotics sooner rather than later. These are: (a) when two or more organ systems are involved *and* the animal is looking depressed, (b) with an exposed bone infection which has not been hosed off many times daily during the first few days and (c) with peritonitis. Peritonitis is an infective inflammation of the abdomen which usually yields a dead cow within a few days. If a vet diagnoses peritonitis, go to antibiotics immediately. If hardware disease is diagnosed (one possible cause of peritonitis), give the magnet and if no improvement is seen within one or two days, start an antibiotic. Cows needing Cesarean sections to deliver a calf have a very high likelihood of developing peritonitis due to the contents of the uterus infecting the body cavity when opened, even if done in a hospital setting.

PROBLEM SOLVING: THE MULTI-PRONG APPROACH

Problem solving, just as in prevention planning, will give better results if not relying constantly on one specific method of approach. It is not far fetched to understand that a variety of approaches to any problem will give a better chance of success. This is what I have termed "the multi-prong approach" as it somewhat conjures up a pitchfork at work. The essence of this approach is holistic. As an extension of this thought, if one pillar of the multi-prong approach isn't working, the other pillars are still in place. In practical terms, think of reliance upon a single insecticide to battle a certain bug every year. If it doesn't work, there are no secondary defenses in place. However, in using a variety of approaches to battle an insect problem, the insect will likely not be able to figure out how to resist multiple angles of attack.

When thinking of the multitude of technically unproven alternative veterinary medicines, I am not too worried if they are not 100 percent effective all the time as I am relying on a variety of methods to restore health as well as hopefully working with animals that are not constantly stressed out by being pushed for maximal production. Additionally, the multi-prong approach to treating anything will likely yield less resistance development from pathogenic germs, insects, plant diseases, etc.

NATURAL TREATMENTS VERSUS ANTIBIOTICS IN RELATION TO ANIMAL WELFARE

It is assumed that farmers can "read" their animals well and that action will be taken early if needed. The whole point of this book is to enable people to read the signs and symptoms shown by their cows such that initial action will be taken earlier than later.

However, it is always the responsibility of the farmer to initiate the action, no one else can do that. Additionally, using natural treatments requires that the farmer be committed to spending extra time with the animal as needed. I have found that most farmers either enjoy the animals more or enjoy the field work more. If you're a farmer that enjoys field work more than spending extra time with the animals, please consider having someone else be the primary animal caregiver for the herd. Using natural treatments also requires that the farmer will not stubbornly cling to the idea of *never* using an antibiotic or be brainwashed into thinking alternatives are *always* better.

In the United States, for organics, federal law states that withholding appropriate medical treatment is illegal. Additionally, farmers should take into account what the consumer would say if they were standing right there talking about the case, when all possible treatments are explained fully.

However, as one farmer said, consumers need to realize that when there is livestock involved, problems can happen. I agree completely. Still, effective treat-ment should *not* be delayed. *Time is a critical factor in whether or not animals will become well again. Therefore, the time that passes until a farmer realizes that a problem exists and the time that passes before the problem is addressed will often dictate the time it takes for the animal to recuperate, if possible, once treatment is initiated.*

Animal welfare should *always* be put ahead of overall profit. After all, the individual animals in the herd are the foundational blocks of the farmer's profitability. Therefore, their well-being is paramount.

KEEP YOUR LOCAL VETERINARIAN INVOLVED

Even though you will learn how to do a basic physical examination from reading this book (see Physical Exam Checklist), please realize that there may be more than one problem needing attention in an animal that is ill. If you have a local veterinarian with whom you work, do not expel him or her from your operation just because you are organic or transitioning to organic. Why? During their medical training, farm animal veterinarians learn how to determine, often only from a physical exam, an exhaustive list of possible rule-outs (differential diagnosis) from which to make management decisions.

In cattle practice, a complete physical exam is the primary goal of any clinician while sometimes blood work is also needed to confirm any suspicions. Indeed, oftentimes there actually is only one primary reason for an animal to be ill, *but* there easily can be secondary effects that need to be addressed as well. Therefore, keep your veterinarian in mind when your animals are not eating, behaving, producing or reproducing as you think they should.

Physical Exam Checklist

- ❏ **Hair Coat & Skin:** glossy coat, dry skin, cold skin, skin twitching, hair up on end, hair color, hair thin or missing, small raised bumps, sore areas, hook bone sores, hock sores, belly sores, calf navel infection, warts, sunburn

- ❏ **Manure:** watery, effortless pipe stream, bloody, bad odor, tinged red, firm, black tar, horse-like, no manure, constantly strains, limp tail

- ❏ **Appetite:** cud in manger, suddenly off-feed, not finishing feed, grinding teeth

- ❏ **Stance:** humped back, head down, humpbacked with fever, one front leg back further than other, very tucked up, lies down a lot, down cow, opens her mouth when pulling up on hair, kneels on front legs, shifts weight on back legs, dipping right hook bone, front legs crossed, cannot lift her back leg off ground

- ❏ **Temperature:** fever, low temperature

- ❏ **Heart:** irregular heart beat, jugular pulses, thickened brisket, jugular groove swellings, swelling behind both jaws

- ❏ **Lungs:** shallow breathing, spongy or crackly feel of the skin, grunting

- ❏ **Eyes:** eyebrow pinch test for dehydration, veins showing in whites, dilated or dime-slit pupils, dull or sunken eyes, growth on the third eyelid, no blink reflex, opaque, solid white, red ring, ulcer or redness in cornea

- ❏ **Ears:** warm ears, cold ears, abnormal direction, sensitiveness, bad odor

- ❏ **Nose:** moist with droplets, dry, pink or red internal nose color, nasal discharge, white plagues in nostrils, bleeding from one or both nostrils

- ❏ **Mouth:** pale, pink, reddish or purple gum and cheek color, loose teeth, ulcers, weak tongue strength, hard and soft jaw swellings, cheek swelling, bad breath odor, mouth swelling, facial swelling, teeth grinding

- ❏ **Abdomen:** silent rumen, hearing a heart beat in the upper left quadrant, pings, pongs, distended left or right side abdomen, papple shape, tucked up, rib cage swelling, swelling in front of the back leg, air detected in abdomen, tight bands, tumors, loops of bowel

- ❏ **Udder:** swollen udder, swollen quarter, swelling in non-lactating animals, hard swelling with watery mastitis, swollen udder lymph nodes, teat cuts, trampled teats, teat blisters, teat-end rings, floaters, blind quarter, abscesses, udder sores, udder skin sloughing, won't dry off, hives when drying off, clots or stringy milk, high SCC, watery secretion, pink milk, mastitis at dry off, gas stripped from quarter, dry cow mastitis

- ❏ **Urine:** urinates often but not much, off urine color, sandy grit at bottom of vulva

- ❏ **Legs:** swelling at hock or knee, swelling on hind leg muscle area, swelling going up leg with fever, lame and lying down

- ❏ **Hooves:** abscesses, bad smell and infection in soft area between hooves, ulcerative sore at hoof-hairline junction, swelling above hoof, swelling above both hooves, swollen ankle, hoof or ankle injury, hoof that is irreversibly damaged, permanent swelling, lines on hooves

- ❏ **Bone:** skinned with bone exposed, broken bone with no bone exposed

- ❏ **Vaginal Exam:** twisting to the cervix and birth canal, only the calf's tail is detected, cow is lying down when calving

- ❏ **Vulva, Vagina & Uterus:** swollen vulva, prolapsing vagina, rips in birth canal, wind sucker, abnormal discharge from vulva, slight red streaks on tail, retained placenta, red discharge from vulva

- ❏ **Rectal Exam**   ❏ **Rumen**   ❏ **Kidney**
- ❏ **Bladder**   ❏ **Uterus**   ❏ **Aorta**

Visually Observable Signs & Indications

Before starting it is important to note that it is always appropriate to compare one body part to its mirror image on the other side in order to get a sense of what may be wrong and to what degree. Likewise, it is always good to compare the way a cow looks to another cow in order to get a sense of difference. Be aware that while it takes a trained eye to catch subtle changes, it is an art and not an exact science.

By utilizing your innate senses of sight, sound, touch and smell you will arrive at a better conclusion than relying predominantly on only one sense. Also, allow intuition to come into play — but it will be to different degrees in different people. For example, clinicians that have been in practice a few years know how to sort out different exam findings yet still may be puzzled. Yet they can still get "a hunch" and can initiate treatment. Granted this hunch is based on examination findings. A problem for a farmer may be that a hunch is based on one primary symptom without taking into account other pertinent factors that help sort out issues, such as: age, part of lactation, housing, feed changes, history of issue, etc.

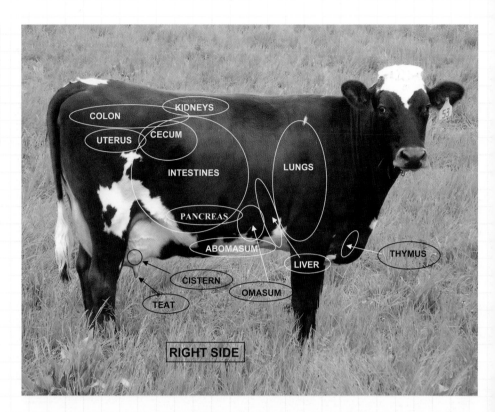

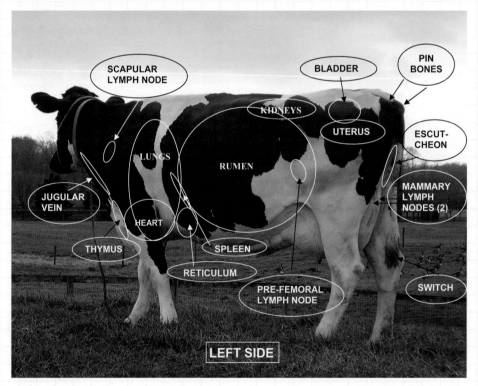

For some very aware and highly conscious individuals, there may be some super sensible signs that guide intuition and help assure that a hunch is correct. In these cases it is still mighty important to take into account directly observable signs that anyone can see.

Take note, the Jersey breed of cows has an amazing ability to "hide" problems until they are further into a situation than does a Holstein. Therefore, it is even more important to jump on problems in a Jersey herd as early as possible!

BODY CONDITION

Cows should have good rumen fill which indicates appropriate dry matter intake to meet their needs. In relation to the stage of lactation — cows will tend to lose body condition and look lean to very lean when in peak milk lactation. This occurs in all breeds but is more noticeable in Jerseys and Holsteins.

Minor breeds and crossbreds tend to keep better body condition during peak milk lactation when fed the same diet as a Holstein or Jersey. If minor breed cows are constantly lean or look skinny, there is a serious feeding issue that needs to be addressed.

Once past peak milk production, animals should start putting on condition again. If they are not, then not enough energy is being fed for what the cow is producing. Therefore, check ration and make sure there is a balance of energy (carbohydrates) and protein.

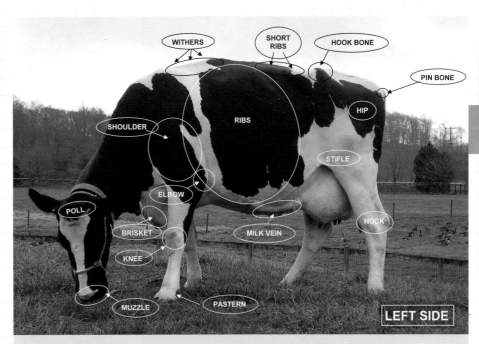

Donna, the author's own certified organic cow and a source of hyper-immune plasma.

Good body conditons of various different breeds of cow.

Good body conditons of various different breeds of cow.

HAIR COAT & SKIN

Glossy Coat — Healthy animals should have a slight shine to their coat. If not, the animal isn't as well as it should be. Note that first calf heifers that freshen in the winter-time will often have an uneven, non-glossy hair coat lasting until spring. Healthy, glossy cows and heifers may show "health stripes" or "happy lines" which are faint horizontal streaks that run across their ribs.

Sweaty Skin — Cows can look sweaty on hot days and that is fine. But, if it's not a hot day and only one cow is sweaty, she may have just broken a fever.

Dry Skin —This is often observed with cows that are out-wintered or with cows that have a chronic problem or are eating an unbalanced ration (especially vitamins and minerals). These animals may also show signs of mange. (See photo on this page of a mangy cow).

Cold Skin — If an older cow is cold to the touch along the back, and just fresh, low calcium is highly likely. Sometimes being cold goes with a feverish condition — so take the temperature and be sure if there is a fever or not. *Cold ears do not substitute for taking the temperature.* Sometimes a cow with scours (diarrhea) will be cold to the touch as well.

Skin Twitching at the Shoulders & Flank — You will see tiny, slight movements or quivers of the skin when the animal is at rest (standing or laying down). In an older fresh cow this is highly suggestive of low calcium. Flies can cause this as well but it is usually a single twitch just as the fly bites. If there are no flies, think calcium. Continuous skin movement over the shoulder area and/or the upper leg occurs as a cow begins dropping in blood calcium but occurs then again when being administered calcium IV.

Hair Up On End — This is seen as hair being straight up and not laying down over the animal as usual. This usually indicates an animal that has had a fever for a little while or is otherwise ill.

"Happy Lines" or Health Stripes: it is as if you ran four finger tips horizontally across the cows ribs. Not easy to see at first, but once you do, you will always know what to look for. The more cows with them, the better. It is an indication of good digestive health.

Dry hair coat, even when on pasture, a symptom of extended poor nutrition throughout the winter.

Hair up on end — this is typical of a cow that has been sick for a while.

Typical areas of ringworm.

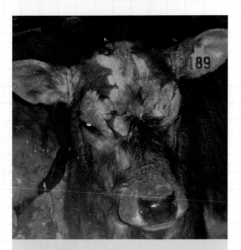

Severe ringworm, the blue is from the farmer's futile use of copper sulphate powder.

Severe mange.

Hair Color — Know the colors of your cows' breed. In a purebred Holstein, black should be black and not reddish black. Reddish black may mean a deficiency of copper or other mineral deficiency or imbalance. It can also indicate parasitism (especially in younger animals with a pot belly).

Patches of Hair Missing or Thinning — You will see less hair over areas or some hair coming up though a thickened area or perhaps a hard crusty scaling where there is no hair. This usually indicates an external parasite problem like lice or mange, especially if in the winter. Ringworm is a grey area at the neck and face and near the eyes, usually in younger animals and at the end of wintertime indoor housing.

In calves, hair loss around the nose and muzzle usually indicates poor milk replacer or poor milk feeding procedures. Make sure that the milk/replacer is being fed at the correct temperature and at regular feeding times.

Small Raised Bumps — You will see small bumps where the hair shaft comes out. This can be due to fly bites with a secondary bacterial infection. These often happen at the shoulders and flank.

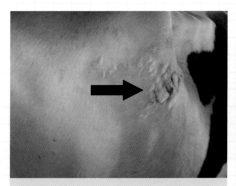

Dermatitis healing and drying with a "leathery" appearance. There could still be active infection underneath what is visible.

Sore Areas — These will be areas that look tan or red, have no hair, have a slight depression and may be oozing a serum-type fluid or even some pus. It perhaps may look "leathery" later when healing.

Sore at Hook Bones — This usually indicates that the cow is lame on the opposite side. She lies on one side too much and causes a rub sore since she won't lie on the painful side.

Sore at Hock — These can be seen as swellings at the hock, which due to friction may open up and become infected. More often, they are sterile and benign. This indicates a lack of sufficient bedding material for the cow.

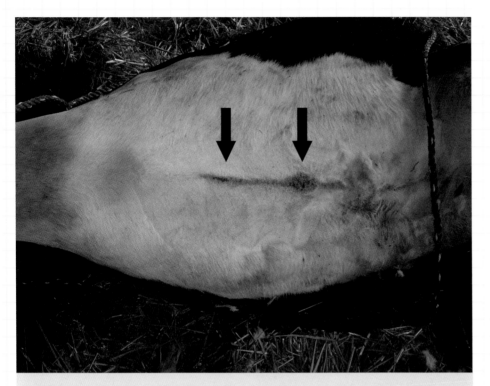

Infectious dermatitis (belly sores) due to flies. Scrubbing with Betadine will help.

Sores Along the Belly — This would be due to flies and secondary bacterial infection, especially in the cooler time of the year with horn flies that cling to the cows' belly.

Skin Infection of Calf's Navel — When a young calf is lame in a leg, there may be a navel infection. Inspect closely. A navel should be dried and "crispy" by five days of age or less. If not, it can become a wick for environmental germs to gain entry into the calf, leading to joint ill and lameness.

Damp, foul smelling navel. Calf is three weeks old.

Warts — Warts will often look like cauliflower-type growths and are caused by a contagious papillomavirus. They are often on the face, near the eyes and on the neck, though sometimes they are on the teats or teat end and the penis.

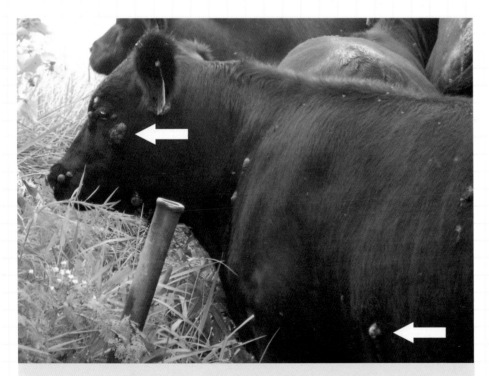

Warts near eye of bull (right), warts on head and trunk of steer (above).

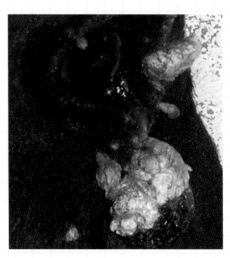

Sunburn of teats on an old cow that had milk fever and was down for a while on a sunny day. Other conditions, like herpes mammillitis can look like this. The end result are usually dried up leathery teats and then mastitis.

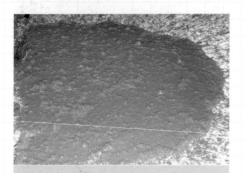

Effortless pipestream diarrhea from a Johne's cow, before bubbles have popped. Typical for Johne's; however, a Johne's positive cow can have relatively normal looking manure too. Be careful!

Cow with bloody diarrhea and fever usually means salmonella infection.

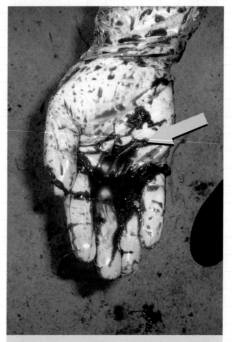

Bloody contents of rectum when removing sleeved hand. Notice the bits of material on the hand — this is sloughed intestinal lining.

Bloody diarrhea, especially with fever, most likely indicates Salmonella (but possibly BVD). In weanlings housed in pens, it could be coccidia (if no fever).

Sunburn — Certain parts of cows burn fairly easily, such as the teats and nose. However, occasionally white areas of fur can be affected — and severely so. Sometimes a poisonous plant may be the culprit. As some plants are metabolized, certain compounds are released by the liver that make the white areas more photosensitive (prone to sunburn).

MANURE

Watery — This is seen as a brown watery blast of diarrhea. This can indicate intake of spoiled ensiled feed or some other problem with the feed being fed.

Effortless Pipe Stream — This will look like thick pea soup coming from a hose, with no straining at all. It is commonly found in cows affected by Johne's disease. However, this can be difficult to distinguish from the manure of cows on lush green grass.

WINTER DIARRHEA

First Calf Heifers — Fresh first calf heifers brought into a barn will experience some new germs. One of the causes is Winter dysentery which is self-limiting and lasts only a few days.

Adults — Animals that break with pipe stream diarrhea in winter should be Johne's disease suspects.

BLOODY DIARRHEA

Bad Odor, Fever, Sloughing of Intestinal Lining and Off-feed — The cow is observed having diarrhea with some reddishness to it and it stinks. Sometimes you'll see some non-manure material in it. This is the intestinal lining sloughing off. If feverish, think salmonella. If not fe-

Black tar-like manure.

Black tar-like manure from cow with right-sided torsion of abomasum.

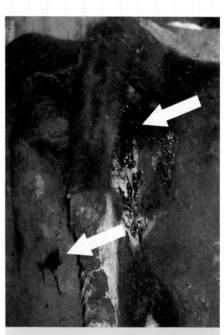
Black tar-like manure on cow.

verish, bovine viral diarrhea (BVD) would be possible. Both can affect more than one animal at a time but salmonella tends to affect fewer animals in a herd generally (but it is more likely than classic BVD).

Tinged Red, No Fever & Eats — With these symptoms think about coccidia. Coccidia irritate the colonic lining and this is what gives the reddish color. It affects mainly young animals just weaned and still indoors.

Normal Manure — Normal manure should set up in somewhat concentric circles without much grain showing or fibrous material.

Firm Manure — If squeezed, water droplets and fiber remain. This is a sign of maldigestion and often is associated with hardware disease.

Black Tar — This type of manure looks entirely black and usually is not in a large volume. It indicates bleeding in the intestine. Digestive processes blacken the blood by the time it exits the animal. This is a very bad sign since internal bleeds are not easy to fix. It can indicate an ulcer somewhere, likely in the stomach/abomasum or in the upper intestine. Sometimes, loose manure or diarrhea that is nearly dark with a hint of reddish will indicate bleeding lower in the gut, namely the colon. This may be associated with coccidia, though coccidia scours usually has some bright red with it.

Horse-Like Manure — This is very firm manure that is difficult for the cow to produce. It is commonly associated with ketosis, with a fresh cow that has been milking really well.

No Manure — If absolutely no manure is on the sleeve after the arm has entered the rectum up to your elbow or further, this may indicate a blocked cow (*i.e.* twisted intestine, twisted cecum, right-sided torsion of the abomasum). Time to call in a veterinarian without delay.

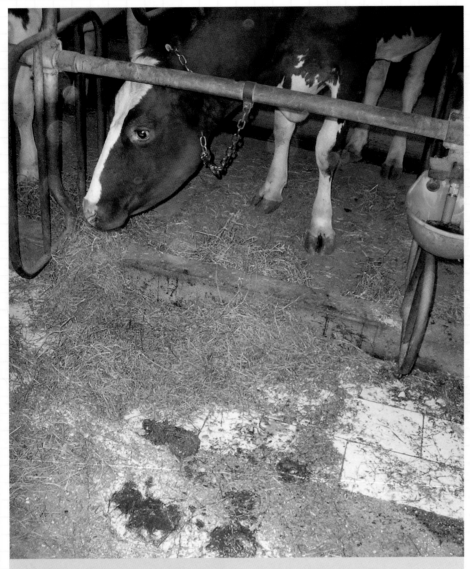

Cud found in manger in front of cow.

APPETITE

Normal & Chewing Cud — At any point in time at least half (and possibly up to as many as 80 percent) of cows in the herd should be chewing cud. When a specific cow is not seen to chew her cud for over 15-30 minutes, there is a problem.

Cud is Found in the Manger — Finding wet clods of cud in the feed manger in front of a cow is not good. This may indicate a blockage in the esophagus, a blockage in the rumen, a tumor in the esophagus somewhere, etc. The cow may be showing signs of mild bloat as well. Cud coming out of the mouth of a cow is never a good sign. Sometimes a wad of cud will be coughed out — if so, don't worry. It is the constant spitting out of cud that should raise a red flag.

Suddenly Off-Feed — If none of the feed most recently offered has been eaten (most easily observed in a tie-stall situation), but the cow eats hay well when offered — this indicates that the cow wants fiber (dry hay). Let her have as much as she wants. If the cow bobs her nose upon the feed — this means that the cow wants to eat but has an internal problem preventing her from taking in feed. This usually indicates an upset rumen, abomasum, or gut problem.

Eats Some But Not Finishing Feed — Usually this is associated with a feverish cow or an intermittent stomach problem.

Grinding Teeth — This indicates that there is pain somewhere, usually in the abdomen. If it is an older cow and she is just fresh, this can indicate low calcium.

STRAINS CONSTANTLY

Recently Fresh — This can be due to uterine contractions or some irritation that occurred during labor and delivery. This can distract the cow from eating normally.

From a Calf — This is usually seen with bloody diarrhea — think coccidia. If the calf is just one or two days old and straining, there could be a congenital defect of the rectum where it has not developed fully. Except for surgery, these are hopeless.

TAIL IS LIMP, NO STRENGTH (NO TAIL TONE)

Older Cow Limp Tail — If the tail is limp (no resistance to being handled) and does not have the strength to move like a normal tail, this can be due to a tumor near the spine or an abscess in the same general area. Occasionally it will be a consequence to a very hard calving (resulting from nerve damage).

STANCE

Normal Stance — A normal stance is a straight backbone and the cow distributes its weight evenly on all four legs.

Humped Back, Head Down — If an arch (slight to obvious) is noticed, especially when compared to other cows, this usually indicates a painful condition, either in the belly or perhaps a limb.

Left front leg held back constantly. Likely heart problem, especially due to hardware if fever is present.

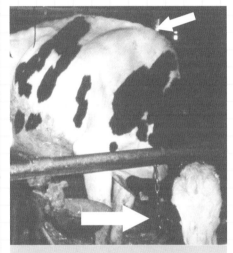

Humped back and head down, likely hardware if quick onset, off-feed, big milk drop and firm manure.

Humpbacked with Fever — With this observation, think of an infection in the belly likely caused by hardware, an abscess, peritonitis or a kidney infection.

Humpbacked with No Fever — Causes include a possible blockage or impaction in the digestive tract or lameness in a limb.

Holds One Front Leg Back Further Than the Other — A painful lower chest likely causes this. Think hardware or something similar.

Very Tucked Up — Being tucked up is often a response to a painful condition in the abdomen.

Very tucked up; very painful abdomen.

Down fresh cow with calf — opens mouth when approached but can't get up. Could be low calcium (notice the dilated pupils), pinched nerve or a fear response.

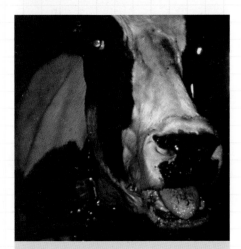

Pulling up on the skin of a standing fresh cow's back and her response is opening her mouth — likely low calcium.

Kneeling continually, will not stand, very anxious stare; obvious pain. This was relieved by administration of butorphanol (an opioid analgesic allowed by USDA certified organic).

Lies Down a Lot — This signifies weakness, exhaustion, and/or pain. It could indicate a digestive blockage that has gone untreated too long (right-sided abomasal torsion, cecal torsion); milk fever (low calcium); lameness untreated for too long (swollen ankle above hoof that is now a bone infection); heat stroke; anemia due to blood loss (cut vein on udder or milk vein); internal bleeding due to ruptured vessel; uterine torsion let go too long with dead, rotten calf still inside; the list could go on and on.

Note: If an animal is laying down most of the time and can get up just long enough for a physical examination and then immediately lies down again, the prognosis is usually grave.

Down Cow — If fresh, think pinched nerve (associated with a hard calving) or milk fever (associated with older cows). My rule of thumb is to keep working with a down cow *if* she is bright and alert, eating and drinking. The moment she starts looking depressed, doesn't eat or drink, starts grinding her teeth, or has urine the color of dark tea, she won't recover. The dark colored urine indicates muscle wasting with muscle proteins (creatinine) being excreted.

Cow That Opens Her Mouth When Near or When Pulling Up on Her Hair Above the Shoulders — If fresh, think about low calcium.

Kneels on Front Legs — This symptom would indicate pain, especially if she stays in this position.

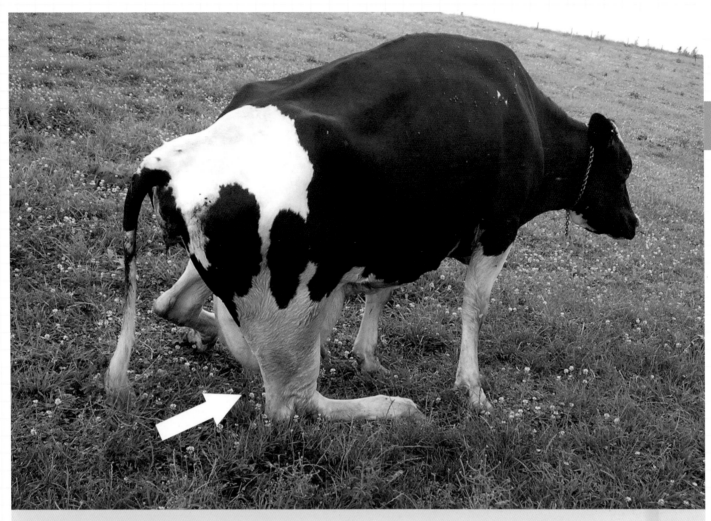

Ruptured gastrocnemius tendon.

Shifts Weight on Back Legs — If the cow "treads" and periodically shifts weight upon each hind leg when standing, this is a sign of colic or abdominal discomfort. Examination is needed that day, especially if not eating normally and less manure production. This indicates that either a more serious gut blockage is occurring or she is having colic due to some bad feed ingested and hopefully she will move it through (most likely as diarrhea).

Dipping the Right Hook Bone Occasionally — When looking at a cow, if you observe that she occasionally dips the right hook bone, this is a *cardinal sign of a right-sided problem in the gut.* If totally off-feed, no manure is seen and she is very full looking in the abdomen, think mesenteric torsion, cecal torsion or intususception and call a vet immediately.

Front Legs Crossed — This is a sign of founder (laminitis) and is occasionally seen in a first calf heifer that has had a major feed change without enough fiber.

Cow Cannot Lift Her Back Leg Off the Ground — This can be due to a ruptured gastrocnemius ligament (the same as our Achilles heel). Salvage the cow for beef.

TEMPERATURE

NORMAL TEMPERATURE

The normal temperature range for a cow is 100.5-102.5 F (38-39 C). On a very hot day, cows may have temperatures up to 103-104 F (39.4-40 C), especially in the late afternoon and still be normal. They are simply too hot as a group and will cool off at night. A temperature of 100.5-102.5 F may not actually be "normal" in a cow that has been obviously sick for a few days — it may indicate her temperature is *falling through* the normal zone to sub-normal and towards death.

FEVER

An individual cow has a fever when body temperatures are above 102.5 F (>39.2 C) and it is not a very hot day. A low-grade fever with temperatures around 102.6-103 F (39.2-39.4 C) may indicate an abscess somewhere (but not always). A temperature of 103.4-104.4 F (39.7-40.2 C) is usually seen with a hot coliform mastitis, respiratory ailments and many other problems. A high fever of 105-106 F (40.6-41.4 C) can be associated with a virus. A temperature of 106-108 F (41.2-42.4 C) can indicate heat stroke, especially if weather conditions would give rise to this. Hose down the cow for 20 minutes, head to tail. A temperature of 109 F (42.8 C) or higher cause brain damage and even if rapid cooling of the cow is done, they usually do not recover.

LOW TEMPERATURE

A low temperature of less than 100.5 F (<38 C) is usually seen in low calcium cows (milk fever), cows that are outside and ill in the winter, or a cow that is near death.

TAKING TEMPERATURES

Traditional vs. Digital Thermometers — Both of these types are fine but realize that the traditional glass thermometers too often break and digital thermometers can die if they get wet.

Taking a Rectal Temperature — Keep a traditional glass thermometer in place for two minutes. Remember to shake it down prior to use. Digital thermometers will beep when ready to view the result.

Taking a Vulvar Temperature — Using the vulva to get a correct temperature is handy if the cow or calf has diarrhea or is otherwise sucking air in and out of the rectum. Taking the temperature in the rectum in an animal with diarrhea will give a false low reading, so use the vulva (and be clean!).

HEART

Normal pulse rates range from 70-80 beats per minute. You can feel the pulse by gently placing a finger on various areas of a cow. Some places are underneath the tail, just behind the jaw, along the neck furrow, just behind the left shoulder blade with a hand upon the chest.

You can also put on a rectal sleeve and feel the aortic pulse.

Is the pulse bounding and very strong? This may mean there is a stagnation somewhere in the circulatory system and can be associated with a fever. Does it have a consistent feel or do a series of pulses "fade away" or is it generally faint and weak? This can mean there is poor circulation either due to the heart itself or a condition that is draining the cow of energy.

Listening to the Heart — Having a stethoscope will enable the farmer to figure out a lot of things. Place the stethoscope just behind the left elbow on the ribs. The normal heartbeat is a constant beat, much like a clock (hence the term "ticker"). The heart rate will be quickened when a fever is present or when there is milk fever (an odd term as there really is no "fever" during milk fever — instead they are usually at a sub-normal temperature; the term probably originates from a cow really wanting to milk but then losing out).

The heartbeat may be slower, but steady, in a cow that hasn't eaten for a while. If it is difficult to hear the heart (muffled), this could mean a fluid buildup around the heart in the heart sac (pericardium). This is bad and salvage should be considered.

Irregular Heart Beat — This is when the heartbeat is anything but monotonously normal. This is usually due to electrolyte abnormalities, milk fever, diarrhea, etc.

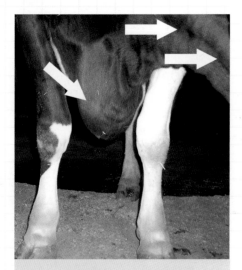

Slightly enlarged brisket swelling and prominent jugular.

Jugular Pulses/Distention — This is seen as a pulse running upwards along the neck furrow. There is normally some of this in every cow but if a sick cow shows this prominently, there is a possible heart problem. Sometimes the jugular vein is very full and engorged. Observe the cow with her head up, as the jugular vein always fills when the head is down (and this is why tying the head downwards helps when putting an IV needle in a cow).

Normal Brisket is Narrow — A normal brisket is narrow with just skin covering the brisket bone between the front legs.

Thickened Brisket — Heart disease may show as accumulations of fluid at the brisket and overly engorged milk veins.

Jugular Groove Swellings — Jugular groove swellings are a raised area usually caused by an attempted intravenous treatment into the jugular vein. Instead of hit-

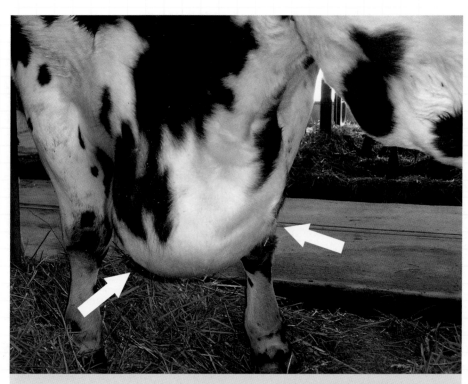

Very enlarged brisket. Likely heart condition and poor circulation.

Note: *An animal vaccinated with the Johne's vaccine will often have an enlarged brisket but due to an abscess full of pus. Swollen briskets are never good.*

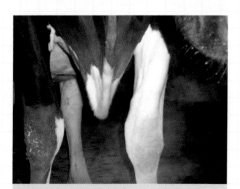

Normal brisket size.

ting the vein, the needle only goes under the skin and causes swelling as a reaction. These can take a couple of weeks to resolve. (It is always "better" to miss the jugular vein and cause a reaction there than it is to miss the milk vein — as the reaction there will be *much worse*.)

Swelling just behind the jaw and below ear (in front of collar) along with thickened jugular vein (seen at low area of neck behind collar).

Fluid Filled Swelling Behind Both Jaws — This can indicate poor circulation due to heart disease.

LUNGS

Normal Lung Function — With normal lung function the chest is seen to expand and relax reguarly. The cow shows no discomfort and displays no extra effort. About 24-28 breaths per minute are normal.

Shallow vs. Full — The chest should rise and fall and be obvious; but sometimes the chest rising and falling is difficult to see. This can indicate pain in the chest.

Abdominal "Belly Breathing" — This is when you see the abdomen rising and falling as the cow breathes but you don't see the chest rising and falling. This is very bad and indicates a serious problem in the lungs or permanent lung damage.

Listening to the Lungs With a Stethoscope — The lungs should sound clear and hollow like a bellows. If you hear a sandpaper or friction sound, this indicates pneumonia. (See cow profile photos to locate lung area.)

"Spongy" or "Crackly" Feel of the Skin Above the Shoulder Blades — Occasionally, there will be a rupture in the lungs and with every breath the animal takes, some free air will escape into her system. Little by little this builds up and will give a spongy or crackly feel to the skin above her shoulders or neck when squeezed. This usually starts when the lungs have been previously weakened and often shows itself just

Lungs (cut open) of cow that had pneumonia as a calf. Yellowish areas are abscesses.

after calving, since the cow strains to calve and ruptures an already weakened air sac in the lungs.

If reaching into such a cow, there will likely be a crackly feel around the kidneys as well and they will hang lower down from the backbone area than usual. This is because air is in the abdominal cavity (where it normally never is).

Grunting — If a cow continually makes a grunting sound with every exhalation, this is *very* bad. Unfortunately it usually indicates that the cow will die within a few hours. Usually a cow that grunts is one that already has been sick or perhaps becomes rapidly ill. There

is not much to do if this is occurring except perhaps provide truly effective pain relief (butorphanol and flunixin).

Note: If a cow has previously had pneumonia and was successfully treated with or without antibiotics but then relapses at some future point — any further treatment is useless. Why? Because lung damage will have been severe and permanent with walled off abscesses. One of these abscesses for whatever reason may have ruptured and be causing tremendous breathing problems in the lungs, which are a vital organ. Foul breath odor may help to confirm this.

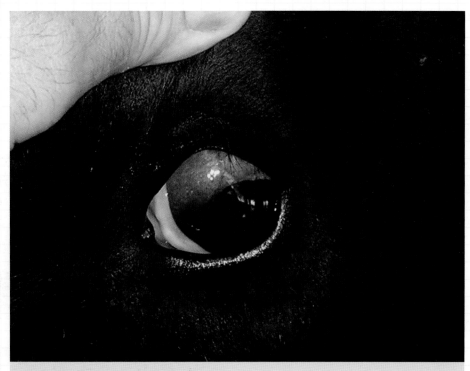

Normal glistening eye.

Pinching the eyebrow of a cow.

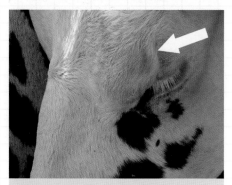

Pinched eyebrow stays tented up — indicates dehydration; IV fluids should be given +/- pump stomach with 5 gallons fluid.

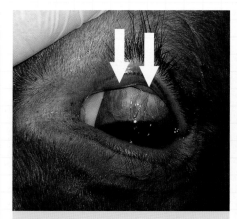

Easily seen veinules, usually indicates toxic cow.

EYES

You can tell a lot about a cow or calf simply by looking at its eyes. Animals normally have eyes that glisten and the animal is attuned to their surroundings.

Eyebrow Pinch Test for Dehydration — By pinching the eyebrow, it is easy to get an idea of hydration status. Normally when pinching the eyebrow, the skin should snap back right away. The longer it stays "tented up" the worse the dehydration. A cow with sunken eyes will usually have a long tenting of the eyebrow when pinched — this indicates that intravenous fluids are needed without delay.

Whites: White or Veins Easily Showing — The whites of the eyes should be just that. In a normal animal, you will be able to see some very thin red veinules that supply the eye with its blood supply. If the veinules are more prominent or show somewhat of a thickened appearance, this indicates the animal is toxic. Again, compare to a normal animal if needed.

Pupils: Normal, Dilated, Dime-Slit — The pupils of the animal, the dark bluish-black central area of the eye, can change shape due to tiny muscles that regulate it. In a dark setting, any eye will be dilated to take in as much light as possible. In a very light setting, pupils will normally be smaller. If a cow's eyes are dilated in regular light conditions, this could mean low calcium, especially in an older fresh cow since calcium plays a major role in all muscles of the body.

By taking a small flashlight and shining it directly on the pupil, it should contract. A milk fever cow will slowly contract, yet not contract fully. In normal light, most cows will have a somewhat rectangular shape to the pupil.

Sunken eyes in adult cow indicate dehydration.

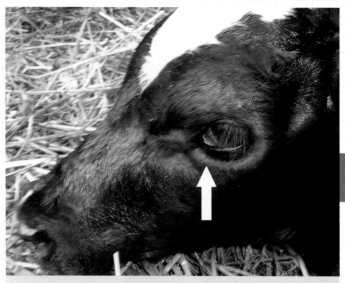

Sunken eyes in calf indicate dehydration. Notice the hollowness of the eye socket. You can nearly place your finger tip between the eye ball and the socket.

If a cow is sick and has only a dime-slit pupil in normal light, along with thickened, prominent veinules in the whites of the eyes, this is a sign of a toxic cow.

Dull or Sunken Eyes — Animals with dull eyes will have a somewhat vacant gaze, telling you that there is something not quite right. Compare them to other animals if needed. An animal with sunken eyes is one where you can see the eye socket without much trouble. This is a seriously dehydrated animal needing fluids (IV and oral) immediately, especially if calves.

Note: The Jersey breed seems to have an ability to hide their problems until they are advanced into the illness. Therefore, when a Jersey cow looks at all sick, she is usually very ill. This has been a consistent finding for me as a practitioner.

Small Growth of the Third Eyelid — This can indicate early cancer of the eye. Small growths of the third eyelid need to be surgically snipped off or these can become severe.

Blink/Palpebral Reflex — Normally when something rapidly approaches the eye, any creature will blink. If they don't this can indicate blindness or paralysis. If touching the eyebrow does not cause the eye to blink, there is a paralysis of the nerve that supplies the eyebrow and usually is associated with listeriosis (circling disease).

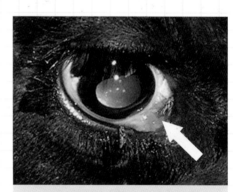

Early cancer eye (squamous cell carcinoma). Nose is to the right.

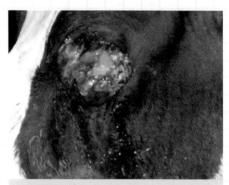

Farmer didn't believe that a small tumor of the eye would eventually destroy the eye (different animal than above).

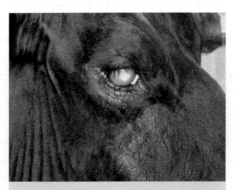

Pinkeye (above) once the intense pain has subsided. The time between symptoms shown in the photos on the left and above is usually when the animal will be squinting from the intense pain from the pinkeye infection.

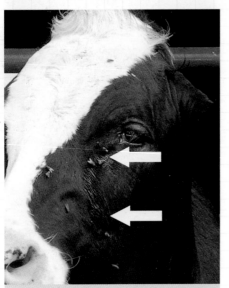

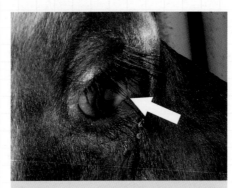

Pinkeye — notice the raised red area in the center of the eye. This area is ulcerated and allowed a portion of the more internal part of the eye to come forth. Notice wet drainage.

Two views of same animal: eye is "sleepy" with moist drainage coming out. This is typical of pinkeye at its earliest stage. Notice flies near drainage. Whether the flies created the irritation and now eye has excess drainage or if the animal accidentally poked her eye on rank vegetative growth, the flies are the known carrier of the pinkeye germ Moraxella bovis.

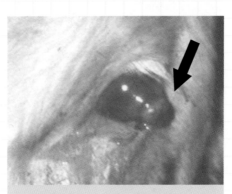

permanent damage from pinkeye; eyeball contents burst forth a long time ago; this is what remains (no vision).

Cornea: Opaque, Solid White, Red Ring Around White, Ulcer, Faint Red — The cornea of the eye is the normally clear area from the surface of the eyeball inward to the colored structures (iris and pupil). If it is at all seen to be anything other than clear, there is an infection going on. Typically in cattle, it will be pinkeye.

Pinkeye can make the pupil cloudy at the earliest stages, becoming a thick white as it progresses, eventually with a red ring around the white area oftentimes. Then there will sometimes be a small ulcer at the next stage.

Sometimes, a sick animal without pinkeye will have some faint reddish patches visible, this is a sign of systemic illness usually as the vessels to the eye are dilated and inflamed.

EARS

Warm or Cold —Feeling the ears is easy to do and a normal animal should have warm ears. However, they may be cool to the touch on cold days if the animals were just outside (just like any person). Too many farmers will declare a cow to have a fever just by feeling cold ears. This is a very inaccurate way to determine fever status (use a thermometer!).

Cold ears in an older fresh cow that is down is highly associated with milk fever; however, instead she instead may be sick with coliform mastitis. Also, a cow or calf that has been cold and wet for too long in bad weather may have cold ears. In this case use a blanket or calf jacket to warm her up. Hot ears may be associated with fever, heat stroke or a hot coliform mastitis.

Notice the different position of the ears. This is a listeriosis case where the right ear is paralyzed and simply lays horizontal whereas the left ear (with ear tag) still has strength to move. An ear infection would give a drooping ear.

Direction of the Ears — Cows will normally have their ears oriented slightly upwards. Cows with both ears that are sagging down usually indicate serious illness (except for Brahma-type breeds which normally have slightly drooped ears). If one ear is drooping and the other normal, check the animal further. If the eye on the same side of the droopy ear is insensitive to your touching the eyebrow and if both the ear and the eye on one side have diminished strength and the animal tends to walk or lean to one direction only, think of circling disease (listeriosis).

Ear Sensitivity (Doesn't Like Ears Being Touched or Held, Will Object) — Normal cows will usually object to having their ears handled.

Ear Odor — Smell the ear canal up close. There should not be any odor. If there is a foul odor this strongly indicates an ear infection. The ear may also be sagging a little and the animal may shake their head occasionally.

NOSE

Moist Nose With Droplets — A normal animal will have a moist nose, sometimes with little droplets of perspiration on it.

Dry Nose — A dry nose is common in animals not feeling well and/or they are dehydrated.

The reddish color to the nostrils should alert the need for closer inspection. Also notice the drainage from nostrils.

Color Within the Nostrils — Pink is the normal color of a nose (if not naturally darkly tinted, like Jerseys). If inside the nostril is very bright pink or reddish, this can indicate a fever or some sort of inflammation of the respiratory tract. If pale, this may indicate anemia. If it is "splotchy" with areas of pale and pink merging, this can indicate a circulatory problem.

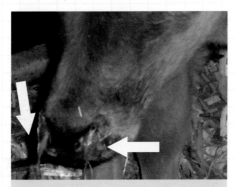

A lot of cloudy whitish discharge in Jersey calf.

Whitish discharge. May not see all the time due to cow licking its nose if not very sick.

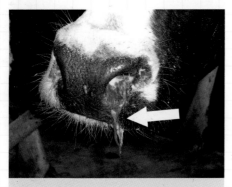

Notice the reddish tinge to the discharge. It was also foul smelling.

Some excessive drainage, more of a cloudy nature.

Same cow as above, notice the bulge of bone on the face. It is an infection, possibly due to sinusitis, tooth root abscess, or trauma. Also notice the semi-closed eye due to the boney swelling.

Nasal Discharge — Most often a nasal discharge indicates a respiratory tract condition (*i.e.* pneumonia). Nasal discharges associated with pneumonia are often whitish. Sometimes a clear discharge will hang down from the nostrils and this may indicate a virus going through the herd, possibly a low-grade hemophilus infection, or excess protein in the diet.

However, occasionally there may be a discharge due to a sinus inflammation or a sinus infection. Sinus infections may yield a discharge with a very bad odor and a swollen facial bone along the nose. These discharges may be brownish with some red tinge.

Note: Anytime a nasal discharge is observed it should *not* be ignored. Hands-on examination and temperature taking is warranted and action should be taken as needed.

White Plaques in the Nostrils — There should be no plaques in the nostrils. If there are, this is a classic sign of infectious bovine rhinotracheitis (IBR) infection.

Bleeding From One Nostril — This can indicate various things but may be due to simple blunt trauma (getting bonked on the head by something). If it is just dripping, use of pro-coagulants may be beneficial. Holding the head up and placing an ice pack on the area near the eye-nose junction may help. Homeopathic phosphorus is very often indicated to use for this.

Bleeding From Both Nostrils — This can indicate a serious, life-threatening, and likely fatal problem. Likely causes can be due to an erosion from a liver abscess into the vena cava (major vein to heart) or a rupture of a pulmonary artery. In either case, there is no hope.

A cow may simply be found dead with a huge amount of blood in front of her face. Fortunately this is not a common problem, especially in herds fed high-forage diets and not pushed hard with grain.

MOUTH

Gum and Cheek Color: Pale, Pink, Reddish Pink, Dusky Purple, Toxic Rings — It is good to look into the mouth as this gives an indication of circulation and general health status. Most cows have pink pigmentation throughout the mouth except for Jerseys, which usually have a dark pigmentation along the lips and just inside the mouth. Pink throughout the mouth should be seen. Sometimes the color will be a pale pink or very pale pink and this can indicate poor circulation (often goes with dehydration) or anemia due to blood loss.

Reddish pink usually indicates inflammation, fever, or excessive circulation. A light purple is not good as it usually indicates a very sick animal. This same animal may have tiny red rings below each of the front teeth – these are toxic rings and indicate a very sick animal.

Note: In newborn calves, there is a brownish red coloration below the front teeth and this is normal — you will need to look at the gums to gauge circulatory status.

Loose Teeth — To check for a loose tooth, you need a special little instrument that keeps the mouth open so that the animal does chomp down on your hand. If the lower front teeth are loose (these are easy to check), this can indicate a chronic kidney condition.

Notice the light purple color of the gums and tongue. This was from a toxic cow with poor circulation.

Toxic rings below front teeth.

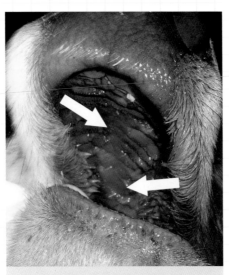

Jersey calf with the roof of the mouth a continual area of red ulceration; due to parasite infestation.

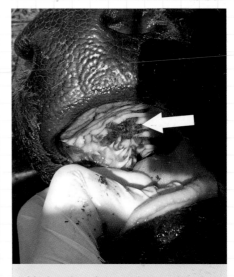

Notice the ulcerated areas on the roof of the mouth. This is from a calf that was barely alive and infested with stomach worms.

Ulcers — If ulcers are seen anywhere in the mouth, this is cause for true alarm. A veterinarian should be called immediately. Ulcers can be circular erosions or ragged erosions. They usually indicate a virus, the most common being bovine viral diarrhea (BVD). Occasionally in a very ill individual calf that is down and anemic due to a severe infestation of internal parasites and not eating, there can be oral ulcers as well.

In any case, oral ulcers are *always* a bad sign. Additionally, if ulcers are found on the tongue, contact the state or federal authorities immediately as this can indicate foot and mouth disease (FMD).

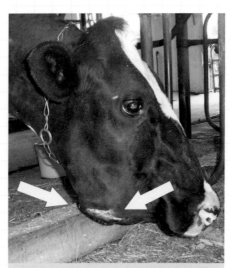

An old case of lumpy jaw with cow able to live normally though the jaw will be permanently enlarged with old scar from drainage at bottom of swelling.

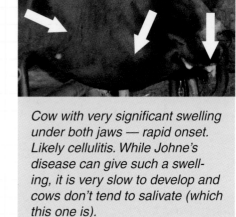

Cow with very significant swelling under both jaws — rapid onset. Likely cellulitis. While Johne's disease can give such a swelling, it is very slow to develop and cows don't tend to salivate (which this one is).

Live cow with botulism: notice tongue hanging loosely out of mouth. This is due to the botulism toxin paralyzing muscles, leading to no strength to pull the tongue back in.

Tongue Strength — It should be difficult to pull the tongue out of the mouth and it should retract quickly. If an animal is off-feed and you can pull the tongue out without objection by the cow, and the tongue hangs out for an extra moment or two before slow retraction, this is a cardinal sign of botulism.

If the cow is still standing, immediate and effective attention is needed to combat the botulism toxins. If the cow is down and the tongue hangs out listlessly, the prognosis is grave.

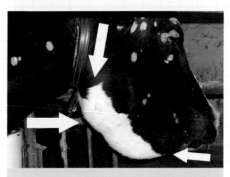

Johne's cow with "bottle jaw" (and ringworm). Bottle jaw swellings usually come on gradually in Johne's cows and is fairly soft to the touch.

Hard and Soft Jaw Swellings — A *hard* swelling on the side of the lower part of the jaw usually indicates lumpy jaw. A hard swelling directly beneath both jaws can indicate an infection at the base of the tongue (wooden tongue) or lumpy jaw.

A *soft* accumulation of fluid in between both jaws can indicate leaky vessels due to a loss of proteins, usually associated with long-standing diarrhea (fluid loss). This kind of swelling, also known as "bottle jaw" usually indicates Johne's disease.

Cellulitis is a dangerous condition that spreads easily when there are no structures nearby to stop the spread. It can be tricky to differentiate between a swelling due to cellulitis and one due to early lumpy jaw. If the swelling is one sided, it is more likely to be lumpy jaw whereas if the swelling is under both jaws and there is a bad odor to the mouth, it is more likely to be cellulitis. Cellulitis can quickly become life threatening and antibiotics are the best choice to treat it. Do not delay. A rare kidney disease called amyloidosis also can cause this but is highly unlikely.

Cheek swelling that will likely open on own.

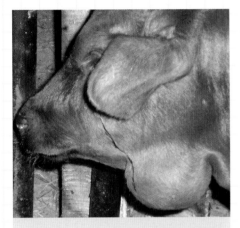

Cheek swelling that may enlarge further and then impede breathing.

Cheek Swelling in Calves — Calves will sometimes get soft swellings due to being pricked by a piece of straw or fodder. These generally are not too much of a problem and sometimes will open on their own or open when handling them and placing a halter on them. On occasion, they can become huge and extend down the neck and hinder normal breathing. The really large ones need to be opened up, drained, and cleansed with peroxide. The swellings that are further back towards the neck tend to be worse as far as enlargement.

Breath Odor — All cattle owners should have a good knowledge of what the smell of normal breath is from normal cud/rumen activity. If there is a foul odor to the breath, consider a respiratory infection or a very upset digestive tract.

If there is a "fishy odor" consider a chronic kidney condition that is not allowing for the normal metabolism of urea to urine occur. Sometimes a cow will have gotten a splinter or something jutting into her jaw or gums and this creates a very bad infection, which can quickly lead to a very bad state.

If there are any greenish boils or swellings found near a tooth or jaw, it is critical that prompt veterinary attention is sought. Some of these cows' heads will rapidly swell to nearly twice the size, oftentimes showing a marked soft swelling under the jaw.

Swelling Inside the Back of the Mouth — Normally there are no swellings at the back of the mouth where the hard and soft palate meet and then end towards the throat. If there are, of if there is a rip, this is usually due to harsh pill gun technique and often causes a very bad infection.

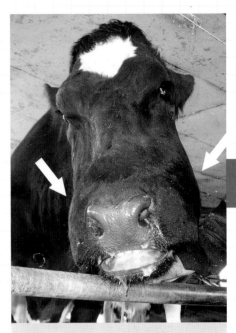

Severe facial swelling that includes areas around muzzle and nose up towards the eyes may indicate allergic reaction.

Severe General Facial Swelling — This may indicate an allergic reaction to a spider bite, snake bite, etc. Eating a feed with a low level of poisonous plants could possibly be involved. The muzzle (length of the entire nose) will be severely swollen.

Teeth Grinding — Cows normally chew cud without much sound at all, if any. Cud will usually be seen along the neck furrow coming up the throat just prior to its chewing. When there is no cud being chewed but a squeaky noise and jaw movement, this is teeth grinding. This indicates pain somewhere, usually in the abdomen. This can also be the result of too hot a ration and ulcers in the abomasum.

ABDOMEN

Rumen Contractions — Listening to the rumen is best accomplished by placing the stethoscope over the triangular area just behind the left rib cage. Normal contractions of the rumen occur every 1-2 minutes, depending on the fiber content of the diet. The less fiber, the quicker the rumen will cycle through contractions.

A rumen contraction will sound like a thunderstorm in the distance coming at you and then the thunderstorm occurs and then it again sounds more distant. If the sounds are more like the surf heard as the ocean hits the beach, this usually indicates a diarrhea or, worse, a possible right-sided torsion of the abomasum (if a ping is *also* heard over a large area of the right side of the cow's rib cage).

A silent rumen that has no action usually requires the use of a stomach tube to feed the rumen to jump-start it. A bloated rumen often will have no activity either, hence the buildup of gas and bloat.

It is always good to use your fist to push in and out behind the left ribs in the triangular area to assess how firm or mushy the rumen is. It should feel somewhat like bread dough prior to baking. If very firm, an impacted rumen may be present. If very soft, an empty or collapsed rumen may be present.

Hearing a Heart Beat in Upper Left Quadrant — When placing a stethoscope in the triangular area just behind the left rib cage, sometimes the heartbeat can be heard. This usually indicates the cow has been somewhat off-feed and the rumen is not full and collapsed enough so that the aortic beat can be heard. An old wives tale says that this also means the cow is ketotic, which it usually is.

Pings — These are "tin can" or "chime" type sounds that can be heard sometimes when placing the stethoscope on a rib and sharply flicking the areas between the ribs. If a ping is heard on the left side of the cow, a left-sided twisted stomach (displaced abomasum) is highly likely about 95% of the time. If the ping on the left is *only* in the triangular area just behind the ribs and below the short ribs, excessive rumen gas would be the other possibility.

On the right side, a ping heard in the triangular area just behind the ribs can be normal in a cow milking well — as the spiral colon is in that area and gas is usually moving through there. However, pings on the right side moving forward towards the front elbow can indicate a twisted stomach (displaced abomasum). If a ping is heard over a large area on the right, use your fist and rapidly push in and out at the belly in front of the right rear leg — if you hear a wavy, splashy sound, this can indicate trapped stomach (abomasal) juices due to a torsion. If in the same cow the rumen is moving but only has sounds like the ocean surf at the beach, this helps confirms my suspicion of a right-sided twisted stomach. Next thing is to check the heart rate — if it is over 120 beats per minute and the animal looks depressed, this is bad. Additionally, if there is no manure on rectal examination, the cow needs surgery without delay.

When I find a cow that is lying down and doesn't want to rise and then has these symptoms as well as lies down again quickly after examination, the prognosis is grave and it is too late for surgery.

Pongs — Pongs are hollow sounds that mean gas is not moving along, as it should (but is not totally stagnant as with pings). A pong is commonly heard in a semi-bloated animal — listen on the left just behind the rib cage in what is normally the triangular area below the short ribs but may now be distended.

Pongs may be heard on the right side and this can indicate poor movement of the intestines, which can be due to low calcium (especially in an older fresh cow). But in a cow that looks sick and is not eating at all, a pong in the lower right abdomen can indicate a twist of the intestine or torsion of the mesentery — both are *bad* and need veterinary attention without delay.

DISTENDED ABDOMEN

Left Side — Usually this indicates rumen bloat, especially if it is behind the rib cage. If severely distended and the animal is kicking at its belly, emergency corrective action is needed. If the bloat is due to ingestion of leguminous pasture for a few days in a row, mineral oil or poloxalene is needed immediately. Usually a few animals will exhibit this. If they are severely bloated and fall down, an emergency stab to the rumen to release the extreme pressure is the only thing that will save them.

If it is an individual animal and not pasture related, passing a stomach tube will often release the gas. This works especially if another person will use their fist to push in and out and also their knee to push upwards as the gas is released by the tube. Passing mineral oil in to lubricate the gut will usually finish off the problem.

If the left rib cage looks a bit "sprung" outwards, a left-sided twisted stomach is possible. Listen for pings. If the entire left side looks enlarged, an impacted rumen may be occurring.

Right Side — The right side of a cow's abdomen really shouldn't ever look larger than the left since it is the left side where the huge rumen is located. However, in a heavily pregnant cow, the lower right abdomen can easily look larger simply due to pregnancy.

GETS UP JUST LONG ENOUGH FOR AN EXAM THEN LAYS QUICKLY DOWN AGAIN

Non-Pregnant — Consider the previous discussion in relation to pings on the right side.

Pregnant — Consider that she is going into second stage labor (active calving) or more likely, especially if off-feed and depressed, that there is a serious complication associated with pregnancy that has not been addressed in time (such as a uterine torsion and the calf is dead and rotten). Any red discharges during pregnancy need to be addressed without delay. *See Internal Exam and Reproduction & Calving sections.*

Both Sides — When a cow has both sides of her abdomen distended, there is usually a serious problem. For instance, if a cow is known to be pregnant and is in the mid to later gestation, a rare but possible constant accumulation of excess fluid in the uterus may be happening (hydrops allantois or hydrops amnion). Or if a cow has been eating on and off for a while and now has been off-feed for a couple of days, a blockage in the gut is possible (especially if no manure has been produced or if no manure is on the exam sleeve when checking her internally).

"Papple" Shape — Standing behind the cow, if her rumen side has the profile of an apple and her right side has the profile of a pear, this is called a "papple" shape.

While the term is a simple mix of apple and pear it unfortunately usually indicates, in a cow that is off-feed, that she has experienced hardware at some point in the past. This silhouette is due to a failure to eructate properly once an abscess associated with hardware injures the nerve that drives rumen contractions. These cows tend to bloat periodically and can be treated with mineral oil (as a "lubricant" for organic record keeping) to get things moving. However, this condition will keep occurring and the animal will be culled when the farmer is tired of treating her over and over.

Very tucked up; very painful abdomen.

Swelling of the prefemoral lymph node, usually indicating cancer.

Tucked Up — This is seen as an animal that looks like it wants to stand to keep as much weight off the abdomen as possible and so stands with an arched back constantly. This indicates serious pain.

Rib Cage Swelling — A swelling on a rib may be due to trauma or possibly a tumor. They usually are benign and simply need to be monitored.

Swelling in Front of the Back Leg (Lymph Node) — The prefemoral lymph node is found in front of the rear leg that is standing normally. This should normally not be visible or should only be a very small bulge. If large and easily seen, a tumor is likely and a veterinary examination for further tumor possibilities should be done.

UDDER

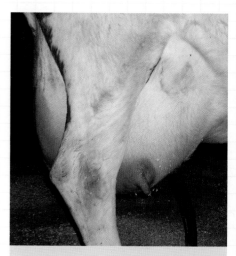

Udder swelling in fresh cow — median suspensory ligament is ruptured due to severity of swelling.

Swollen Udder — The udder is one of the main parts of a cow the farmer sees close up everyday and usually can notice subtle changes. Swellings, by definition, are mastitis (inflammation of the udder), regardless of what the cause is. The reason for the swelling is of course the important thing to sort out. Only the typical "bagging up" a week or two prior to freshening is normal. Also, heifers will develop their udder over a few months during late pregnancy but also really bag up like a cow when calving is near. It is important to observe for evenness of swelling and not a lopsided swelling. Lopsided swellings deserve attention the moment they are observed due to likely mastitis. *See Swollen Quarter.*

Fresh Cows — Cows that are fresh normally have a swollen udder. Excessive swelling can be the result of a few things and can be independent of each other. Edema is certainly common, especially in just fresh heifers. Edema is a fluid accumulation that when pushed in by a finger will leave an indentation. It usually is not painful to the touch but certainly looks painful oftentimes by its size.

Swollen Quarter — This is usually obvious to any dairy farmer. The degree of swelling and type of swelling can help in determining a course of action. Any swollen quarter should have its contents expressed to observe the type of secretion. If a cow is running a very high somatic cell count, either detected during monthly dairy herd improvement association (DHIA) testing or via the California mastitis test (CMT) paddle, but the milk looks fairly normal, strep ag (*Streptococcus agalactiae*) is a real possibility. This is even more likely if the bulk tank count has been running high for the last few months (500,000-700,000).

While antibiotics can quickly eliminate this germ, this kind of bug can wreak havoc on organic farms if strong corrective management changes are not taken along with treatments aimed at the quarter and animal's immune system.

If there are stringy discharges, these can be due to many different germs and a milk culture should be taken to determine if it is an environmental germ or a contagious germ. It is *always* best to culture milk to accurately determine the type of mastitis causing germ.

Unfortunately, however, not all milk cultures will grow colonies. However, this is no excuse not to try to accurately determine the source of infection.

Swelling in Non-Lactating Animals (Dry Cows or Heifers of Any Age) — In a cow that is dry, an un-bred heifer or a bred heifer, a secretion which has an odor and usually a yellowish pudding-like material, is almost always due to *Arcanobacter pyogenes*. When observed, the quarter is already irreversibly damaged and the idea is to make sure the cow stays well enough to not abort, if pregnant. Usually there is significant fever. Occasionally, especially in dry cows, the swollen quarter will lose proper circulation and gangrene sets in. If the secretion is watery, the condition is usually due to coliform mastitis or possibly an environmental streptococcus. In dry cows generally, the cause is an environmental type of mastitis germ.

Hard Swelling vs. No Swelling With Watery Mastitis — While a swollen quarter is not a great sign, a cow with a watery secretion (likely coliform) with no swelling at all is actually worse. This is because a swelling at least indicates the body's defenses are at work while no swelling may indicate the animal's defenses are totally caught off-guard and the germ is not stopped at the local area in the udder but more quickly has escaped into general circulation. Usually, there is at least a mild swelling in most cows exhibiting irregular milk. This is good, to a point.

Swollen Udder Lymph Nodes — There are lymph nodes called supramammary lymph nodes on the right and left side of the highest area on the backside of the udder. These may be enlarged during a mastitis incident on the same side. You can feel these. If, however, an older cow without any mastitis has palpable (detectable by manual feel) supramammary lymph nodes, cancer is a real possibility.

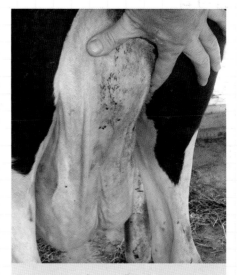

Swollen supramammary lymph node in a cancer cow; however, in any cow with mastitis, a swollen supramammary lymph node is possible.

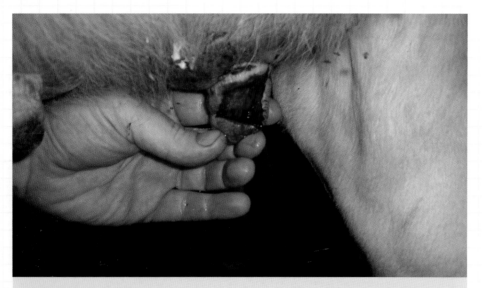

Turning down flap of teat that was cut. Cow needed to be sedated with xylazine and butorphanol to inspect this and clean it up before snipping off the flap.

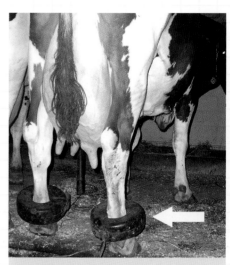

Udder donuts can prevent a cow from accidently stepping on her own teats.

Teat Cuts — If a cow has a cut on her teat and it is leaking milk out the side, stitching is necessary to correct the problem. It is vitally important to get it stitched within about six hours so inflammation does not hinder stitching and appropriate healing. If the teat is too far damaged, then cutting the teat off may be the best course of action. However, be aware that every time the cow lets her milk down, milk will flood out what was that quarter. If the milk canal is not involved and there is basically a nasty deep cut of the teat, stitching will really help to resolve the problem (again, do not delay due to inflammation setting in).

If there is a cut and the result is a triangular type flap, it should be snipped off if the base of the flap is towards the bottom of the teat and it can be stitched if the base of it is towards the top of the teat. This is because the circulation to the area comes from above, not below.

Tramped Teats — Unfortunately, teat ends can get stepped on and essentially smashed for whatever reason. This will hamper milk outflow. The teat really needs to be opened up with a special little instrument designed to cut and catch excess material in the way of the milk canal. Constantly inserting dilators and drains will very likely cause mastitis of the worst kind. Udder donuts can prevent a cow stepping on her own teats by accident.

Teat Blisters — Occasionally, especially in cold northern climates, freshening heifers will experience blisters on their teats. This usually indicates a herpes mammillitis viral infection. These can be extremely bad as untreated teats become hardened and leathery, which makes milking difficult, if possible at all. Mastitis is a common result. Fortunately, it is usually only one quarter but it is still a terrible way to have a fresh heifer enter into lactation.

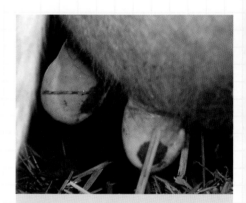

Blisters on teats — early herpes mammillitis. This stage is rarely observed. Usually only the "leathery" teats are noticed when milking.

Aloe gel with a little tea tree oil would be highly appropriate as well as dipping with a glycerin based teat dip. *Teat blisters occurring at the same time as blisters at hooves and in the mouth would be a high alert for foot and mouth disease (FMD).*

Teat end ring — indicates fluctuating vacuum during milking (or over milking, if only one teat).

All 4 teat ends are prolapsed, indicating fluctuating vacuum levels during milking times.

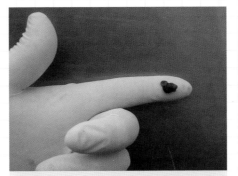

Floater expressed from teat. No cutting of teat needed. Consider the size in relation to the index finger (approximate size and shape of a teat) and the size of a teat opening.

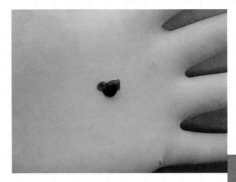

Teat-End Rings — Occasionally, a cow (or many cows in a herd) will have a small circular ring around the teat end of every teat on the udder. These indicate either keeping the machine on the cow for too long (over milking the cow) or there may be odd fluctuations of the vacuum at the teat end during milking time. Either way, these rings are actually prolapsed teat sphincters.

Normally the teat sphincter keeps the teat shut from outside germs; however, when the teat ends are prolapsed, outside bacteria have easy entrance into the teat. These cows often will have higher somatic cell count (SCC) than herd mates. This kind of damage can occur in very little time (days) but takes a long time to heal (months).

Floaters — These are pesky little globs of a fatty-type material that for some reason occur but only rarely. When they do, the teat will milk out nicely until the floater becomes lodged at the teat sphincter. These can be worked out manually. Manually express milk until the floater gets lodged, then "clamp" off the teat up high while also working out the floater through the sphincter. This certainly can be tricky and a veterinarian can usually get it done fairly easily. Also, have the cow's tail jacked up or have the cow very mildly sedated as they do mind the procedure generally.

Blind Quarter — Heifers sometimes come fresh with only three functional quarters/teats. This is almost always due to having been sucked on by another calf when they were young. Oftentimes the quarter will actually feel identical to the others, though upon close examination it will appear very slightly firmer. Moreover, when rolling the teat between your fingers, you will feel a little core or string like feel in the center of the teat running the length of it. This is definite evidence that the teat and quarter are permanently and irreversibly damaged and non-functional. Do not try to open one of these up — it would be like opening a can of worms.

A normal teat, when rolled between the fingers, will have a hollow feel running the length of the teat where the intact milk canal is.

Abscesses on the Udder — The udder should be symmetrical. Sometimes an abscess or a lump will appear, especially upon a quarter that has had mastitis previously. If this is the case, the cow probably either has *Staphylococcus* (Staph) *aureus* (contagious) or *Arcanobacter pyogenes*. While the abscess may or may not open up, be aware to keep that quarter out of the bulk tank and out of the normal milking machine (use a quarter milker) since the somatic cell count is usually very high.

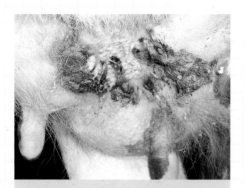

Udder sore. Clip area, scrub vigorously with Betadine and or chlorhexidine, then apply a drying powder. Never apply a salve to these areas as it will trap in germs that like low oxygen conditions.

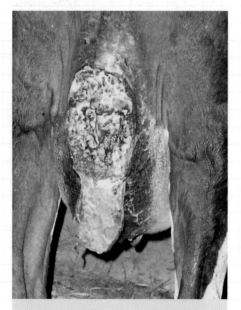

Udder skin sloughing due to severely swollen udder when fresh.

Udder Sores — On some fresh cows and heifers, especially those with very large and edematous udders, sores will develop between the udder and the leg or between the two halves of the udder. These are very difficult to heal but cleansing with apple cider vinegar may be beneficial and then applying a drying powder to the area. The germs that inhabit these areas like moisture (most germs do) — therefore it is entirely useless, if not worsening, to apply a salve or cream to the area.

Udder Skin Sloughing — This is rare but is due to poor circulation and a severely swollen udder when fresh. Cleanse the exposed area and give it time to heal.

Won't Dry Off — Some cows just won't quit milking when it is time for them to "go on vacation." Dry off really should be a once stopped then done deal. Not a once a day milking for days on end situation — for the message to the brain to stop milk production won't occur if milking once a day. Feeding only straw will certainly cut down on milk production.

If they have excessive body condition, check to make sure they are actually still pregnant. Most pregnant cows will not be overly fat at dry off time. If she is still pregnant and due in a couple months, then feed her only straw for 24 hours. Straw on its own will not make milk but will keep her filled up. Do not feed any energy or high protein feed; it will only continue to help make milk. Also, if during wintertime, withholding water for 8-12 hours will help reduce milk production (but never withhold water otherwise). Never, never do this in the summer. The best way in the summer is feeding straw for a day or more.

Hives When Drying Off — This is called "milk allergy." Sometimes with Jersey or Guernsey cows, an animal may show hives or a wheal and flare type reaction to stopping being milked. This is a rare reaction to excess milk proteins staying in the animal when they otherwise were being harvested at milking time. Homeopathic Ledum 30C has helped with this.

Calf that was sucked on and has two swollen quarters. Compare to other side where the normal right hind teat can barely be seen.

Down cow with watery secretion; turned out to be gangrene when gas was stripped out shortly after picture was taken. The teat was very cool to touch and "flabby" feeling.

Udder Development in Unbred Heifers — Sometimes a group of young, unbred heifers will develop a small udder. This is often due to eating highly estrogenic plants (legumes such as clover or alfalfa) during pasture season. Of course it is a good idea to get these animals checked for pregnancy status to make sure they are not bred too early. Sometimes a bull may have slipped under the wire!

These small udders will be symmetrical in shape. If one quarter is swollen, it is likely mastitis and due to having been sucked on earlier in life. The quarter, though needing to be stripped out, is permanently damaged and non-functional — she will in all likelihood be a three teater.

Clots or Stringy Milk — This indicates that the quarter is reacting to an irritation, which is most likely a germ that has triggered the animal's immune response. It should be pointed out that a "shed-down" will look like this. A "shed-down" is essentially a quarter or gland ridding itself of excess accumulations. A true "shed-down" occurs when a therapeutic is administered at a distant site (like under the skin) and the quarter reacts and releases pent up accumulations.

However, please realize that whenever an irritating substance is infused directly into the quarter, a reaction can occur and what a farmer may think is a "shed-down" may in actuality simply be the gland locally reacting to what was recently infused. Regardless, clots

Clots in milk indicate mastitis. Always keep such quarters out of the bulk tank. Consider a quarter milker. This cow's discharge had an obviously foul odor. There is only one kind of mastitis like that — arcanobacter.

and stringy secretions must be kept out of the bulk tank. Also, this very poor quality milk is bad to feed to calves.

Tri-plate showing a lot of Staph aureus growth in upper section. Notice the hemolysis (pale band surrounding the individual colonies) running alongside all the colonies — this is classic for Staph aureus.

Tri-plate showing many individual colonies of Staph in upper section and one long streak of Strep uberis (circled) in lower section.

Tri-plate with lots of Staph growth and lower section showing some individual colonies of Strep ag growth (circled).

High Somatic Cell Count (SCC)

— Milk is routinely tested by milk companies at pick up or through monthly testing programs to check udder health — the higher the somatic cell count, the worse the udder health.

Somatic cells are cells from the animal's immune system that have entered the gland in response to challenges. Milk cultured from high SCC glands will often show bacterial growth, but not always. It is always good to culture poor quality milk in order to know what germ is involved — for this will help with management and control of the problem.

There are generally two kinds of germs that farmers should be aware of — contagious and environmental. The contagious germs (staph aureus and strep ag) have a strong affinity for the udder and live there quite well, setting up shop, so to speak.

The environmental germs (all coliforms, strep dysgalactiea, strep uberis, enterococcus spp., coagulase-negative staph) normally live outside the udder. Both types enter the gland through the teat.

Typical management of environmental outbreaks seeks to identify and correct likely weak spots regarding proper milking preparation and the cows' bedding environment. Typical management of contagious mastitis outbreaks relies upon sanitizing the milking equipment after milking known infected cows as well as milking those cows last. Pre-dipping and post-dipping with an effective teat dip as well as wearing gloves are also always appropriate.

Please keep in mind the different climates of different regions. Just because something works or is typically done in a certain region or part of the world does not mean that it automatically translates to being appropriate for your farm. If something is broken, it needs to be addressed and fixed.

California Mastitis Test (CMT) —

This is a purple solution that reacts with a milk sample and gels/thickens if there is a high somatic cell count in the quarter. It is a reaction between the CMT liquid and excessive proteins in the milk. In generally, a CMT kit will have the solution (as a concentrate needing dilution) and a paddle to squirt the samples into. I have found that holding the paddle so that the actual handle of it points directly backwards (in the direction of the cow's tail), will always let me know which quarter is in which of the four collection areas.

CMT plate — the left hind quarter is thicker looking and has a darker color, however the right hind quarter is also bad, though less so. By holding the plate under the cow so the handle is in the direction of the tail, you will always know which quarter is which.

Mas-D-TEC — measures electrical conductivity of milk to determine SCC.

With the paddle level, swirl it around and look for thickening or gelling. Then turn the paddle over and watch the milk drain off. It should drain off like rain water droplets and not as thick strings. CMT kits are essential for good milking management.

Another reason to use a CMT is that the milk company only checks the bulk tank and monthly milk testing programs only identify somatic cell counts at the cow level — but neither show which quarter is involved! Additionally, knowing which quarter actually has the high CMT will allow you to culture the appropriate quarter as well as to use a quarter milker to keep that quarter's bad milk out.

An alternative to the CMT paddle is the Mas-D-Tec device that immediately gives a fairly accurate SCC count. It is much more expensive than a simple CMT paddle and liquid.

Watery Secretion — A watery secretion or one that looks somewhat like lemonade is never good and needs prompt attention as it usually indicates a coliform mastitis. Oftentimes the quarter will be swollen, firm and warm (perhaps even hot to the touch). The cow will likely be off-feed and depressed but also possibly kicky when checking the quarter. It is a painful condition that cannot be ignored. It is plain dumb to ignore it and leads to nothing good.

Treatment aimed at the quarter itself is limited to applying external lotions (especially the cooling mint products) rather than infusing anything into the quarter. Stripping out the quarter to rid it of the terrible bacteria and breakdown materials is of utmost importance. Stripping frequently throughout the day is required. Other treatments are aimed at the cow's general system and are listed under *The Non-Antibiotic Treatment of Infectious Disease.* This requires IV fluids, biologics and strong botanical preparations.

Note: A watery quarter that is *not* swollen is a true problem as it may indicate that the germ hasn't triggered the immune system and may have slipped into general circulation quickly.

Pink Milk — This is self-explanatory, although sometimes pink specks may also be present in pink milk or white milk. In either case, this indicates a ruptured vessel somewhere in the vicinity of the quarter. These generally self-cure if given enough time, however as with anything dealing with animals in production, the quicker the return to normal the better.

In these cases, pink milk either happens due to another animal ramming its head into the udder of the affected cow, the affected cow itself bumping into something, the cow racing around outside with its udder swinging wildly, or possibly due to weakened internal vessels associated with aging or maybe a tumor or other pathologic process. In any event, it is important to keep the cow still and not walking around as this may continue jarring the vessel that is ruptured.

When called to a cow that has not resolved in a few days, I will use vitamin K1, 100cc under the skin, to help coagulation of blood. If the cow is older, I will also give calcium, as it is part of the normal clotting mechanism and may generally be low in the older lactating animal.

Do not give aspirin or flunixin as these substances inhibit clotting. Using a cooling peppermint lotion would make sense too.

Mastitis at Dry Off — Cows coming to the end of lactation and experiencing a clinical case of mastitis (flakes, specks, clots) need effective treatment prior to drying off as do cows that have dramatically increased on the somatic cell count.

Drying off is a somewhat stressful time for any animal and the immune system dips temporarily. Anything that stimulates or positively augments the immune system, especially if given a few days prior to actual dry off, should be helpful. Using a soothing botanical udder infusion like Phyto-Mast as an antiseptic would be wise on problem quarters.

Gas Stripped From Quarter — Gas stripped from the quarter indicates that gangrene is setting in. This is a *very* bad sign and indicates one of two possible causes: clostridium infection or staph infection.

Gangrene mastitis is associated with fresh cows that do not have good udder circulation, usually due to excessive udder edema/swelling. Sometime it is seen in dry cows as a secondary infection after a hard quarter occurs from Arcanobacter.

In any event, any treatment undertaken must be *immediate*. Outcome depends on a few factors: the age of the cow (the younger the better), standing versus laying down when first found (standing is a much better — laying down is a very bad sign), and the degree of fever — a high fever of 104 F to 105 F (40 C) is much better as it likely indicates a staph infection and that the animal's immune system is responding.

A low fever (102.7 - 102.9 F (39 C)) indicates a likely clostridium infection and rapid systemic involvement of toxins.

Note: A down cow with gas gangrene mastitis that will not get up and grunts with each breath will likely die within a couple of hours despite any treatments attempted (conventional or organic).

Dry Cow Mastitis — Mastitis in dry cows is often associated with leaky teats and is due to the natural plug of the teat end loosening up (within two weeks of freshening) or the plugs not having yet formed (within two weeks of dry off). The usual types of germs involved are from the environment where the dry cow is laying around and typically are coliforms. Tramped teats can yield this condition as well.

Occasionally, and more likely during the summer, a cow well into the dry period will get a mastitis and these are generally an Arcanobacter. These unfortunately are not usually noticed quickly (as dry cows are not checked as closely as lactating cows) and the disease process is well under way. These animals will have a high fever (as will coliform cows), which may trigger an abortion of the calf. Treatment should be aimed at the entire cow, as the quarter will already be permanently and irreversibly damaged and non-functional.

Teat Dilators & Teat Tubes — While teat dilators or teat tubes are occasionally needed to drain a quarter due to the milk canal becoming constricted, continued use of such devices undoubtedly leads to mastitis. When using these, utmost attention needs to be taken in regards to cleansing the teat end with alcohol prior to insertion and using single use disposable dilators or teat tubes.

It is likely that the veterinarian needs to "open up" these kinds of teats using special instruments and maintain sterility as best as possible. Even then, a damaged teat (which initiated the need for a tube or drain) is a likely source of infection itself.

URINE

Obtaining a Urine Sample — Analyzing the urine of a cow is basic to a complete physical examination. Obtaining a sample is best done prior to the exam since the cow may become uptight and not urinate later. To get a cow to urinate, take a handful of hay and methodically massage the lower vulva and area below that. Sometimes a cow will only give a few drops but then other times she will gush forth a lot. Sometimes by simultaneously massaging between the short ribs (kidneys are below them) and also using the wad of hay below the vulva, urination will begin.

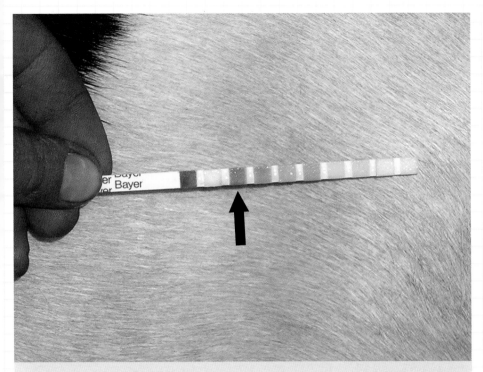

10 way urine analysis strip. Third square from thumb is the purple of ketosis. First square (greenish-brown) near thumb indicates glucose in the urine — this photo was taken a just a couple minutes after an IV of dextrose was given.

Sandy Grit (Crystals) at the Bottom of Vulva — Sometimes a bit of pale yellow crust is seen at the bottom of the vulva. If you go to feel this between your fingers, it will likely feel sandy. This indicates a urinary tract infection. The sandy crust will possibly have a strong odor.

Ketones/10 Way Dipstick — Urine dipsticks to check ketones are easily available at farm stores or through your veterinarian. These are very handy to have on hand as diagnosis of ketosis is a basic need for dairy cows.

Ketones in the urine will turn a dry white pad purple to varying intensities. The deeper and quicker the purple development, the more strongly ketotic the animal is.

Some veterinarians will use a 10 way urine analysis stick. These help to confirm suspicions found during physical examination. These are handy since occult blood (unseen blood), white blood cells (indicating infection), specific gravity (salt balance/dehydration), protein level and pH can be detected.

A normal cow should have an alkaline pH whereas off-feed cows will have acidic pH. If a cow has an acidic pH, ketosis and is off-feed, a commonly associated finding is a twisted stomach — either then or within a day or two.

Urinates Often But Not Much — This usually indicates a urinary tract infection. A urinary tract infection may be in the urethra, bladder, ureter or kidney.

Urine Color — A deep yellow is sometimes seen in dehydrated cows (but they will not urinate much at all) and does not have much significance. Tea-colored urine, especially if seen in a down cow that has not been able to rise, is a very bad sign as it indicates that there is muscle breakdown and the proteins of the muscle are being released into the system and excreted in the urine. If

seen, it is time to quit trying, as the animal will not rise again.

Reddish urine will be seen in bladder or kidney infections and indicates blood in the urine. Colorless urine is a common finding and usually indicates a cow that is drinking water normally or excessively. If a confirmed pregnant cow has a reddish discharge, she should always be checked to make sure that the pregnancy is still OK. If the pregnancy is OK, then the reddish discharge is probably due to a urinary tract infection and if the cow is otherwise normal, no action is needed.

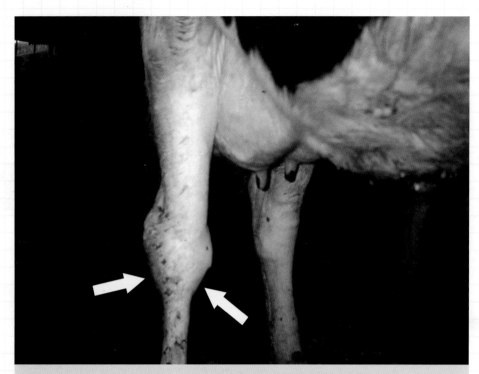

Complete hock swelling, on both inside and outside of hock. This is generally worse for the cow than a swelling just on the outside.

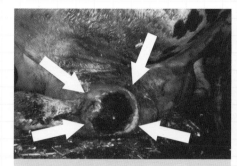

Very infected hock (purple around black central area).

LEGS

Lameness is critically important to monitor for — with individual cows and also at the herd level. Much like general body condition of a herd, the amount and severity of lameness in a herd is very revealing of good overall management (or lack of it).

Any animal that is visually lame needs attention. This is even more critical in grazing herds for obvious reasons. Prevention of lameness is accomplished by various means. Many lameness problems are due to hoof problems.

Swelling at Hock (Hind Leg) or Knee (Front Leg) in Adults — These swelling problems are usually due to damage, either from not enough bedding (hind leg) or from lunging forward upon rough material to get up (front knee). Putting these cows out to pasture will give the best possibility of it clearing up.

Do not open up these swellings since they are often a sterile inflammation. Opening these up as you do an abscess will actually invite germs into the area and make it a lot worse.

Swelling on Hind Leg Muscle Area — Swellings up high on the hind leg are almost always due to a muscle site injection that is infected and has become an obvious abscess. Poor hygiene (cleanliness) of any part of the injection technique can be a cause. This could include a dirty bottle top, a re-used needle, and probably the most likely, by going through an area of hide that is not clean. Additionally, I have found that abscesses are often due to large quantities of vitamin C injections (never put more than 30cc in any one spot).

Further down the leg, at the end of the large muscle area is a lymph node (popliteal) that can become swollen. This can be secondary to an infection somewhere in the leg or a poor injection technique going too low in the hind leg or more rarely, due to lymphosarcoma (leukemia) which involves lymph nodes and their swelling.

Damp, foul smelling navel (calf at right). Calf is three weeks old.

Swelling at Hock (Hind Leg) or Knee (Front Leg) in Calves — This condition can be seen in calves that are usually about two to four weeks old. It usually involves a front knee, although a hock (hind leg) can be involved. Swellings in this age class are almost always due to a navel infection within the first few days of life, which, for unknown reasons, settles into the knee joint (or hock). These are nearly impossible to cure except perhaps with high doses of antibiotics.

Why are joint infections so hard to treat? This is mainly due to the protected nature of the joint apparatus itself — there is little blood supply to the area to either support the joint or to battle infection.

Calf with navel infection and secondary painful lameness in hind leg (healed well with penicillin treatment).

Swelling Going Up the Leg, With Fever — If the entire leg is swollen in comparison to the other leg, this can indicate cellulitis. This is bad as cellulitis is an infection just under the skin that can rapidly spread. Prompt treatment is needed. I have seen some farmers use 250cc vitamin C IV and 4-8 oz. colloidal silver IV (one time) with good results.

Lame and Lying Down a Lot — An animal that is lame and lying down a lot usually means they have been going slowly downhill over time. With a cow that has been observed to be lame, this usually indicates that there is a severe infection in the ankle with its origin in the hoof or as an injury at the hoof-hairline junction.

HOOVES

Hoof health initially depends on proper nutrition but is also dependent on the environmental conditions. One particular kind of lameness, caused by ulcers, is especially disheartening because this is ultimately caused by poor ration nutrition and will usually affect a high percentage of the herd. Additionally, the genetics of the animal will dictate the general strength of the hooves. Those animals with black hooves will generally have fewer problems than those with white hooves. This is due to the different composition of the hoof itself.

The importance of correcting a hoof problem the first time cannot be overstated. A botched attempt can leave a cow in worse condition than she was prior to any intervention. Therefore please note the following sections.

Inspecting an Individual Hoof — If an animal is lame, and especially if she will not put full weight on a hoof when walking the hoof needs to be inspected to determine what is wrong. Proper restraint of the animal is critical in order for the leg to be lifted and to be able to manually handle the bottom of the hoof (the most likely area of problem). Short-tie the cow and place a rope slipknot above the hock and pull up the leg.

When looking at the bottom of a normal hoof, you should be able to place the entire outside perimeter onto an imaginary board. The middle area of each hoof should look "dished out" towards the outer perimeter. Immediately take note of any raised area on the sole — this

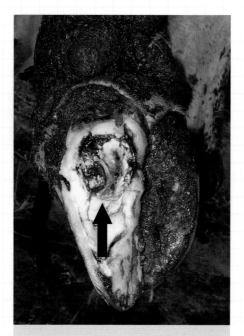

Hoof abscess pared away to show large area near heel as site of abscess.

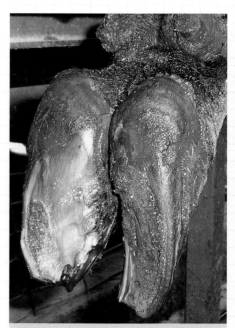

Abscess pared away at the white line area (junction of wall and sole).

indicates an area of the sole that hasn't had normal wear and tear, likely due to the animal not putting weight there. To inspect this, pare away any raised area in order to restore the normal shape of the hoof. This will often reveal the bad spot, likely an abscess.

Abscesses — An abscess is an accumulation of pus or other foul material, usually due to an infection that has lodged in that part. Abscesses are common in hooves. Abscesses in general are not difficult to treat as they are towards the surface of the body. However, especially in the hoof area, an abscess can spread internally to include the ankle joint, which is extremely difficult to treat effectively.

Most abscesses on the sole of the hoof will have a black streak leading to it. Pare away the black streak until it ends. It likely ends

with a small spurt of fluid (any color, but often brownish-tan). This means the abscess has been found and ruptured, which affords prompt relief to the cow, even though she will be objecting to the work being done. Don't stop — the abscess needs to be opened up. Open up the abscess until there is a good junction between the visible sole and the internal layer. You should *not* be able to slide your fingertip between the sole and the more internal layer.

Once the abscess has been found, I will sometimes pare away about half of the sole of a hoof. Most, but certainly not all, abscesses will be somewhere of the middle of the hoof towards the heel. However, if a cow goes lame very quickly (usually this is different from *you* only noticing it "just yesterday"), the abscess, if there is one, may be up front toward the very point of the toe. Always check the "white line" area for ab-

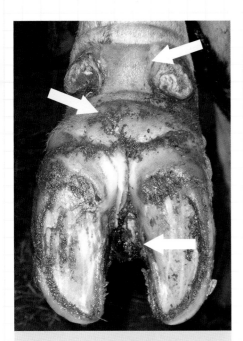

Foot rot is always between the two toes. Whenever an interdigital corn is ulcerated, foot rot is sure to follow. Notice the very inflamed purplish pink area above the hooves — this indicates infection of the entire joint.

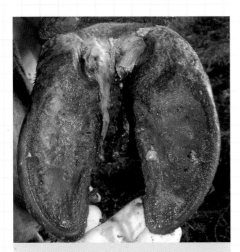

A foot rot case after the first wrap has been removed. A dead ropey core of cheesy tissue fell out when cleansing and revealed the above.

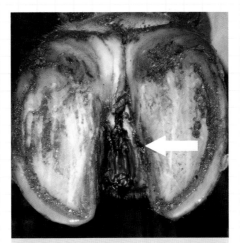

Same hoof as left. Foot rot due to ulcerated interdigital corn (cut out to get rid of problem and to bring new circulation to area).

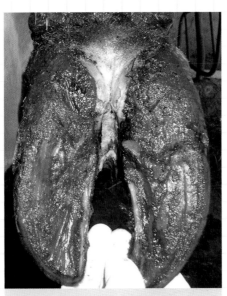

Same foot rot case as in the left photo after the second wrap has been removed. Just four days later. A very noticeable improvement is seen by smaller area and pink color. A final cleanse and wrap were applied and recovery was complete.

scesses. This is where the sidewall of the hoof meets the bottom (sole). In a white hooved animal, there is a thin white line that shows. If there are any defects, pay attention to that area and pare it away to possibly find an abscess. Abscesses are one of the most common problems in hooves.

Bad Smell and Infection in the Soft Area Between Hooves — This is foot rot: a condition that affects the soft area *between* the two hooves. While it is considered to be contagious, I have found it to be more closely associated with areas where rocks may injure that soft area between the toes causing an infection to set up. The area will look irregular and have a deep crevice or rut, which will stink upon closer inspection. Running your finger through the area will cause the animal to retract the entire foot.

Oftentimes (and sometimes extremely quickly) the ankle area above the rot will become swollen due to the infection spreading. These need to be effectively treated without delay. With some regularity I will see foot rot with an animal that has an interdigital corn (a growth between the toes) that is usually benign until an injury (like a stone) punctures the growth and a foot rot sets in.

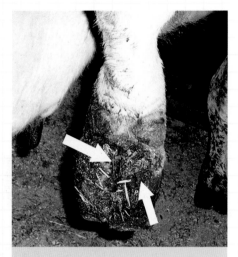

Unwashed hairy heel wart at hoof-hairline junction (1).

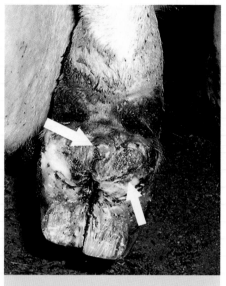

Hairy heel wart pared — notice it is affecting both sides of the heel (2).

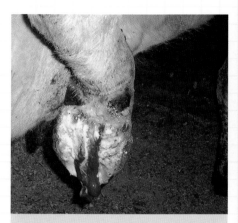

Hydrogen peroxide fizzing action upon what was hairy heel wart (4).

Typical site of a hairy heel wart at hoof-hairline junction

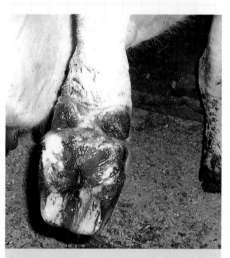

Hairy heel wart pared and washed (3).

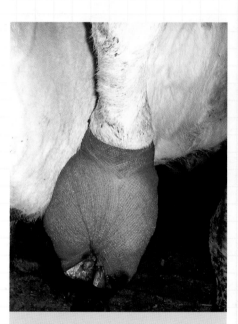

Hairy heel wart wrapped with Betadine and sugar mix on cotton below hoof wrap (5).

Ulcerative Sore At the Hoof-Hairline Junction (Often With a Crusty Scab Over It) — This is strawberry or hairy heel wart. This condition *only* occurs at the hoof-hairline junction. It is either an erosion or an excessive growth of moist, inflamed tissue which then crusts over. No single agent has been shown to cause these for sure,

though a Serpens bacteria can be associated with the lesion.

Since no single agent is involved and the lesion always occurs somewhere at the hoof-hairline junction, we need to think about what may be involved. It should be pointed out that the hoof-hairline junction is a sensitive area in that it is a major anatomical boundary. Things that can cause irregular hoof growth will affect the area as well as poor perfusion of blood supply to the area.

Nutrition comes to mind of course. Excess grain (or an imbalance of forage and grain) that can acidify the rumen and damage it may release potentially toxic materials through the rumen walls into general circulation. These could accumulate in small yet damaging amounts down at the hoof-hairline junction area and impair the normal health of the area. Add to this an area of manure where cows are standing and the conditions could be ripe for the typical hairy heel wart lesions to emerge.

Another nutritional angle would be herds that do not have a balanced ration from a mineral point of view — not enough calcium, phosphorus, zinc, etc. to support healthy hoof growth from the hoof-hairline junction.

Swelling Above One Hoof — This usually indicates an infection in the hoof directly below the swelling. Lift the hoof and closely inspect the hoof for an abscess or other problem.

Swelling Above Both Hooves (the Entire Ankle Joint) — This kind of swelling is most likely to occur when an animal has foot rot as the infection can quickly enter into the ankle soft tissue area. Additionally,

the entire ankle can become swollen if an infected hoof is neglected for too long and the initial swelling above the one digit essentially crosses over into the entire ankle area. It is easier to treat a swollen infected ankle due to foot rot than due to an abscess that has been neglected.

Swollen Ankle — Occasionally, especially in grazing herds, a cow will simply twist its ankle out in pasture. She'll be lame but no problems in the hoof are noticed nor is there swelling extending from hoof-hairline junction on up. Only the ankle is involved, with normal areas directly above the hoof/hooves themselves.

Hoof or Ankle Injury — In barns with gutter grates, injury due to the cow getting her toe stuck in the grate is possible. This is usually a very bad injury as it can result in a fairly deep gash in the area at the hoof-hairline junction and/or a hairline fracture (broken bone) of one of the bones in the ankle or hoof. The only way to stay ahead of these is to thoroughly hose the area down at least three times daily for the first few days to keep it clean. Think about all the germs that are around gutter grates. Keeping germs away by repetitively and thoroughly hosing the area (many times a day the

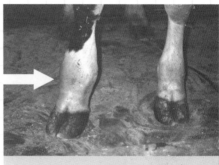

Likely twisted ankle. Notice no swelling immediately above hoof at hairline junction.

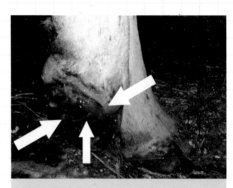

Hoof-hairline injury — never good and almost always leads to severe infection.

first few days) is your best chance at staying ahead of the infection.

If the injury was seen to happen and then a few days go by until the animal is obviously lame, critical time has been lost and these animals almost never recuperate — the best chance for recovery is if penicillin is given without delay.

Leg immobilized for good access to amputate. Cow is on her back. (1)

The process of amputation using gigli wire. (2)

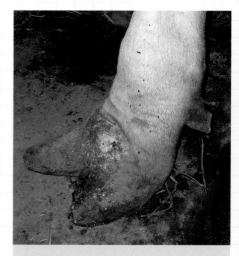

Permanent damage but the cow functioned OK.

Stump of hoof after amputation. (3)

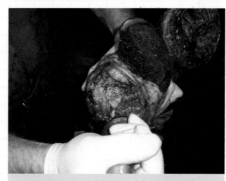

Cauterizing amputated stump to stop any bleeding. (4)

Betadine and sugar mix. Keep it thick. Commitment to re-wrapping stump twice weekly for one month is required post amputation. (5)

Final outcome of a successful amputation. Cows can live for many lactations afterwards. (6)

Hoof That is Not Fixable or Has Irreversible Damage Needing Amputation — Sometimes a digit (one of the two toes) is too far damaged to be able to fix. In this case, amputating (cutting off the toe) will be curative because the toe will not grow back. This should only be done by a veterinarian or a hoof trimmer. The best candidate would be an animal whose digit is not repairable and yet *not swollen above the hoof.*

Animals needing a toe amputated can do very well for many lactations after recuperation. Wrapping of amputation stump *must* be done twice weekly for one month to keep the healing area clean and not infected. Increased swelling in the ankle above the toe to be amputated decreases the likelihood of a successful outcome. This is because swelling in the ankle means there is infection in that joint, which can run up the tendons and never be effectively cured without antibiotics.

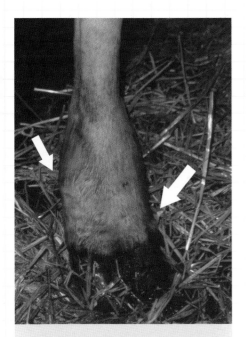

I had given up hope on this cow. She was down and had been on penicillin by another vet. I switched to homeopathic hepar sulph and then silica and slowly but surely the cow improved but had a permanently enlarged ankle area.

Permanent Swelling After Convalescence — Sometimes an infected hoof, ankle or leg will very slowly heal, but only to a certain point. This will be seen as a firm swelling in the area. Most animals can move fairly well but will nonetheless be permanently impaired to some degree.

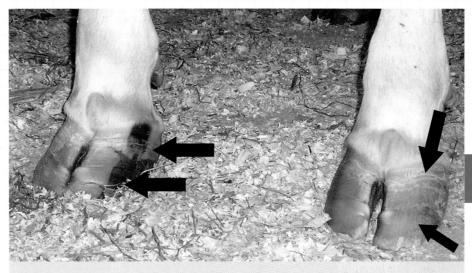

Notice the different areas of growth along the hoof wall on these toes. This is evidence of a major stress (usually a nutritional change) in the animal's diet.

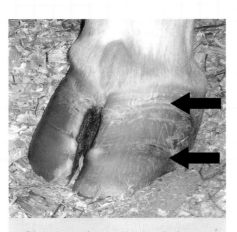

Close-up of same animal above.

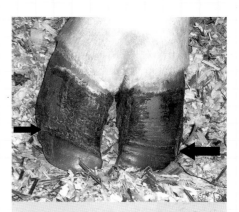

Animal from same herd as (above). Usually all hooves will be affected.

Lines on Hooves — Hooves grow from the hoof-hairline junction downwards. It follows that any imperfections of general hoof growth are due to problems originating from the hoof-hairline junction.

Imperfections of hoof growth show up as lines. These lines indicate different types of growth, usu-ally due to stresses placed upon the animal(s) — especially dietary stresses. If you see an animal with all four hooves with lines all equally below the hoof-hairline junction, this animal has endured a significant dietary stress. This is usually a feed change for the worse i.e. high grain or lowered mineral content.

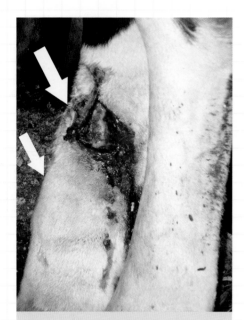

Serious infection let go too long (neglect) — notice the dried area of skin and swelling below the exposed bone (compare to other leg on same animal).

BONE

Skinned With Bone Exposed — Exposed bone is self-evident and is also very bad. Infection is highly likely. While I have seen one or two cows whose long bones have been exposed eventually recover without antibiotics, most that are not treated with antibiotics do not make it. The idea is too keep these areas exceptionally clean, possibly by hosing with water if the animal will stand still for it — three times daily *starting immediately.*

Uncommon but not unusual is to see one of the large hook bones (at the top of the cow) be exposed, mainly due to trauma. These are tricky in that exposed bone can lead rapidly to generalized infection and

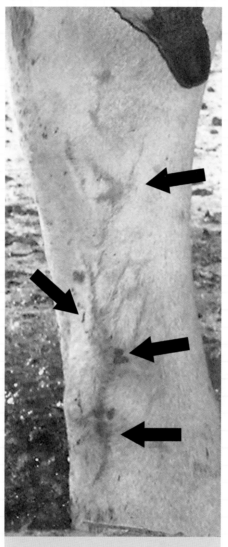

Healed exposed bone infection. Excellent care and conscientious involvement of extra labor to keep area clean is critical for positive outcome. Scar line indicated. Different animal than shown on left.

poor outcome but occasionally the hook bone being exposed will not give as much trouble (if kept amazingly clean and antiseptics are used *early* and continually).

Calf with broken ankle due to hard pull by farmer at birth . You must immobilize the joint above and below the break. In this case a simple long U shaped piece of PVC was placed behind the leg to support it, then cotton was liberally inserted to cushion the leg, and then a few rolls of Elasticon kept it in place. The cast is left on for four to five weeks.

Same calf as above, immediately after cast removal. The obvious excessive angle to the ankle corrected with exercise over time.

Broken Bone Not Exposed Through Skin — This is called a simple break. The bone may be broken in a few different places, but it has not punctured through the skin. *Broken bones heal best in calves.* The key is to immobilize the joint above and below the break — *this is critical.*

Heifer with broken ankle. Flies gathering nearby a suspected tiny cut (dark spot) guided the decision for immediate slaughter, since gangrene would likely set in once a cast would be applied (low oxygen to infected area).

Broken ankle up close to show the skin break and open area.

INTERNAL EXAMINATION

(With Obstetric Sleeve On) — One of the classical pictures that people have of a dairy veterinarian is a person up to their armpit reaching into the backside of the cow (with a plastic sleeve on, of course!). One doesn't have to be a licensed veterinarian to do this on his or her own cows. Obstetric (OB) sleeves are cheap and should always be on hand. There are two ways to reach into a cow, either vaginally ("directly" as I usually say it) or rectally. And actually I find it odd when a farmer calls for a calving problem only to find out when I get there that they haven't even reached in directly to at least attempt to figure out the problem (if any) — sometimes everything is perfectly normal and a vet would not have been needed.

An odd situation that sometimes occurs is the cow's hook bone mysteriously is no longer there. At some point it must have been broken but not protruding through the skin. These don't seem to bother the cow too much for it is only after the fact that it is noticed. The bone must have been reabsorbed into the system. It is truly amazing how self-cure can occur — just don't get lazy and expect self-cure to happen with your animals every time.

Casts for legs can be as simple as a semi-circle of PVC that is long enough to immobilize the joints immediately above and below the fracture wrapped with Elastikon elastic tape. There are much more complex types of casts. For a calf, a cast needs to be on for about five weeks.

Broken Bone — Exposed Through the Skin, Even if Only a Puncture — This is called a compound fracture. This is at extremely high risk for infection and withholding antibiotics is *not* appropriate in this kind of case. Even the slightest suspicion of a small pinpoint area of torn skin is very bad. Whether or not the animal should be treated at all may become the question and humane euthanasia (putting the animal "to sleep") is a realistic and understandable option.

VAGINAL EXAM

Pre-Calving — Reaching into the vagina of the cow is always a wise thing to do when suspicions about calving occur. Get a halter on the cow and tie her in a corner some-where. Corners are best so they can only swing around 90 degrees in-stead of a full 180 degrees if tied to a long length of a gate or wall. Allow about 12 inches of halter lead be-tween her nose and the tie spot and also tie the halter fairly low, maybe 3 feet up from the ground. Tying the cow in this way will allow the cow to lie down easily if she wants to — but be aware that whenever doing ob-stetrical work it is *always* easier to accomplish things with the animal *standing* — always!

Put an OB sleeve on, have the tail out of the way, wash up the back area well, put some lube on your palm and wrist area, then reach in with your hand in a vertical position the same way the vulva is oriented. A springing first calf heifer will greatly resist this as she has never had a calf pass through and your hand is rather big for her yet.

Cervix — This is the first item to check. The cervix is the tunnel with connects the uterus to the vagina/birth canal. It can be felt at first when you are up to your wrist at your fingertips as a round fibrous ring. It is tightly closed all during pregnancy and then opens up to allow the calf to be pushed out. The cervix will be completely open when the calf has been bumping up against it due to the mother's contractions. It will become as wide in diameter as the vagina/birth canal. If it is not,

Pulling a calf and having the legs crossed to torque the calf helps ease pas-sage of large hook bones. Calf's head is hanging down since its backbone is offset compared to cow's backbone. Having head hang down also allows for mucus to drain from nose and mouth.

and the calf is still in the uterus, do not simply pull on the legs to get the calf out – this is *very wrong*. This is especially wrong to do in a springing heifer that is beginning to calve. Al-low time to dilate more.

Delivery — The cardinal rule is *never, ever* rush a springing heifer. Trying to get a calf out too soon, especially in a first calf heifer with a very tight, never-yet-expanded birth canal is the cause of so many problems in first calf heifers. And what a shame, in a moment of impatience, two years of rearing an animal becomes severely damaged because the farmer is in a rush to get the calf out. Which is worth more — the soon to lactate heifer or the calf? Only in embryo transfer is the calf "worth more" than the dam.

My rule of thumb is to *never* pull a calf out of a heifer until the calf's

nostrils are fully outside and visibly exposed, as accomplished by normal contractions of the heifer in labor. Why? Because by the time the nose is fully exposed, the large crown of the head will usually have naturally expanded the birth canal enough for the rest of the calf to be extracted.

If a calf is pulled from a heifer in labor when just the tips of the calf's hooves are exposed, the never-yet expanded birth canal cannot accom-modate the relatively large head so suddenly. Once the head is fully out and the legs are fully out, *stop everything for a moment and cross the front legs*. Then resume pulling and always in a downward direction to the laboring heifer's heels.

It is critical to make sure that the calf's backbone is *not* directly under the cow's backbone but offset slightly (*i.e.* 11 or 1 o'clock to the cow's backbone). This will definitely help the calf's wide hook bones come out more easily. This will more likely prevent hiplock, the usual reason that a heifer is paralyzed and cannot get up after calving.

An Older Cow Delivery — Older cows will have already had the birth canal and cervical tunnel expanded at least one time from previous calvings, and it is somewhat OK to get a calf out sooner than with a first calf heifer. But still, it is best to wait until the nostrils are fully exposed from the vulva.

However, older cows may not advance due to reasons other than a tight birth canal: namely low calcium or a fetal-maternal mismatch where the calf is simply too big for the cow carrying it. In cows that are fourth calf or older, a slow calving is much more likely to be due to low calcium blood levels. If there are cold ears and some muscle twitching at the shoulders or thighs, low calcium is extremely likely, and giving a bottle of calcium IV prior to calving will help.

Twisting or Auger-Like Feel to the Cervix and Birth Canal — When a farmer calls and says that the calf feels too far in and the cow has been trying to calve for a couple of hours, a very common finding (especially in Holsteins), is a twisted uterus/ uterine torsion. Additional to the auger-like feel to the birth canal will be that the cow has had her tail extended out, something like a gasoline pump handle.

These signs are classic for a uterine torsion. Do not delay — get the vet as a cow will *never* calve on her own when this is occurring. If the cervix is fully open and there is no twisted uterus — simply feel which parts are where. Oftentimes a leg will be turned back or the head will be turned back. This needs to be corrected with "gentle strength" — enough strength to move things around but not too much force to rip things mindlessly.

When turning a head towards the front it is important to cover the lower teeth of the calf as they are sharp and can slice the uterine wall if careless. Legs need to be rearranged as needed and the best way is to cover the hoof so it won't tear anything. Always move the limb somewhat toward the center of the calf as you correct it. *Always* have the cow standing when rearranging limbs, if possible. You need to have as much flexibility and area to move limbs around as possible — having the floor pushing up will limit your work area within the uterus.

Only the Calf's Tail is Detected — This is a true breech presentation and can be very difficult to correct, even for a veterinarian. Once you have determined where the hock of the back leg is, the rump needs to be pushed forward to give enough room to quickly grab the hock when possible. Then slowly bring the hock up towards you. Once it is at the "tipping point" of going forward, you need to quickly grab and cover the hoof as you pull the hoof up towards you while making sure the hock tips forward more. The second leg will need to be done the same way but there will be more room once the first leg and hoof are correctly laying upon the floor of the birth canal.

It cannot be said enough: always have the cow standing when rearranging limbs!

Cow is Lying Down When You Try to Help Calve Her In — It is much more difficult, if not at times all together impossible, to correct problems in a cow that is lying down. If needed, give an older cow calcium IV first to get her up before rearranging the limbs or head. Have a shocker on hand to see if the cow will get up. Also, use the shocker if she seems like she is going to fall over the moment you have finally gotten to the point of correcting a limb. Once the legs and head are correctly aligned and within the vagina/birth canal, it is then OK for the cow to lie back down. But make sure that the head is in the birth canal first (through the cervix and through the uterus).

Sometimes, you will need to gently push the last cervical ring (nearest you) up and over the crown of the calf's head. This is valuable to do if the calf's head is almost through the cervix, but not quite. Massaging the cervix over the crown also means that there should be time given for the head to then expand the birth canal. Having pushed the last cervical ring over the head, stop and allow about an hour for things to expand. In older cows, low blood calcium can lead to weak contractions and a difficult calving. An older cow with cold ears that is down early in the calving process (when the calf is still completely in the uterus), which cannot rise even with electrical stimulation probably should get a bottle of calcium IV.

Twins. Notice the yellowish color on one twin — this is meconium staining (the first manure a newborn makes) and indicates the calf was stressed in-utero prior to delivery. This calf was stuck and needed re-positioning. Reaching in afterwards revealed a twin. The cow was about one or two weeks earlier for projected calving date (common for twin situations).

Checking the Cow Right After Calving — After the cow has calved, always give her a 5-gallon bucket of cool water right away and refill as needed. A normal cow will often slurp down 10 gallons of water quickly. I don't like it when a cow is left with just a small water bowl to drink from in the corner of the box-stall. Add homeopathic pulsatilla to the water.

Once a cow has calved, always check for a twin. It is absolutely terrible to have a twin stay in a cow to die and essentially rot over the next couple of days. Any cow that freshens one or two weeks earlier than her expected date likely has a twin.

When checking for a twin, it is then also a good time to feel for any rips that might have occurred as there won't be as much swelling as in a few days to come.

Once the cow has drunk a couple buckets of water, try to get the cow up. Why? This does two things: (1) it tells you if she can get up or not and (2) this can help prevent a prolapsed uterus since a standing cow will keep the uterus down in the belly rather than a lying cow that can easily flop it out if she keeps straining (like a first calf heifer) or if all her muscles are weak from milk fever (in older cows).

VULVA, VAGINA & UTERUS

Normal Discharge After Calving — A cow that normally passes her placenta within six to eight hours after calving will then have a very thick, golden sticky discharge the next couple days. This is what you want to see.

Note: If a cow does *not* pass her placenta within six to eight hours of calving (for whatever reason) — and even if she does pass it all on day two or three — she will go on to have a uterine infection 99 percent of the time. So just because a cow passed all the placenta at day four does *not* mean that you can forget about her as it will mean that you must cleanse the uterine environment out as much as possible prior

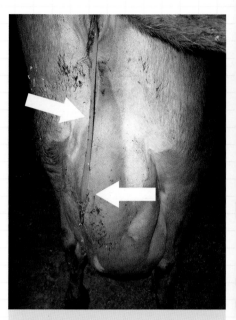

Normal discharge from a cow one or two days fresh that calved and passed the placenta within eight hours of calving.

Normal discharge from a milk fever cow that passed the placenta normally.

to the closing of the cervix (usually occurs a couple days after the placenta passes, regardless if it passes on time or if assisted at day five or six post-calving).

Swollen Vulva — The vulva of the cow can become swollen due to various causes. If she is near calving, this can be a normal change, though excessive swelling sometimes is seen, especially with first calf heifers. If not hugely swollen, this should not hinder the normal calving process since the vulvo-vaginal ligaments loosen up as labor approaches. If excessive and very firm to the touch, use of an herbal diuretic to eliminate fluid may be helpful.

In cows that have just freshened and have a swollen vulva, this can indicate a difficult calving took place, with associated trauma and a likely rip of the birth canal. If this is the case, serious infection usually quickly takes hold. General systemic treatment of the animal is needed to arrest the process from worsening. Cows that are aborting may show a swelling of the vulva just prior to the abortion and shortly thereafter.

Prolapsing Vagina — In dairy cows that are within a couple weeks of freshening, the ligaments can loosen up too much and too soon. This will be noticed as a pink softball-sized mass that shows itself when the cow is lying down but disappears when she gets up. These are generally not a problem and clear up after calving since it is mainly due to internal hormonal changes associated with the end of pregnancy.

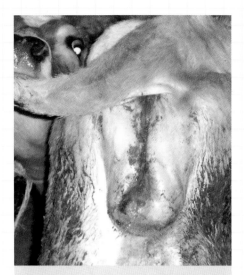

Swollen vulva is common when there is an internal rip of birth canal. Reaching in and out of these to place uterine pills aggravates the condition and hinders healing of vaginal lining.

However, sometimes these become excessive and remain after calving and become a serious problem. They will enlarge, stay protruded when standing, become stained with manure — which then dries upon the mass making it filthy. Sometimes excessive post-calving straining will create this situation. If a cow is just fresh a few days and the pink softball-sized mass hasn't disappeared fully, seek veterinary attention, as it will likely worsen.

Rips in the Birth Canal — Rips and tears are not an uncommon consequence of a hard calving, especially in first calf heifers. If there is severe swelling that feels very tight when you are reaching in vaginally, *stop*

and *do not advance farther* as a rip can become extended by your hand expanding a very tight area. This is not a good situation, but using anti-inflammatory medication would be indicated.

Too Much Air Goes In and Out of the Vulva — This is called a "wind sucker" and is a cow in which too much air goes in and out of the vulva and into the vagina. This will usually be noticed when the cow has been fresh a couple of months. You will hear air movement when the cow gets up and down. This will be seen in cows that have a tilted vulva — usually in slightly older cows. It is an anatomical defect that will hinder getting the cow bred back. Once fixed via a Caslick's procedure, most cows will breed back.

This is a heritable condition that means that her heifer calves may eventually have the same condition. However, it is a rather simple condition to fix. The vulva is surgically sewn together with just enough opening for the animal to urinate and to allow breeding.

Bear in mind that if an animal is sewn shut to cure the wind sucker condition, the vulva needs to be carefully opened up with a scalpel prior to the next calving otherwise there will be a jagged opening created by the calf as it is expelled through the scar tissue that formed to keep the vulva shut.

Cow fresh three weeks, excessive lochia (bloody mucoid discharge).

Notice the "sunburn" look to vulva — this denotes chronic irritation and likely uterine discharge from infection (notice buildup on tail).

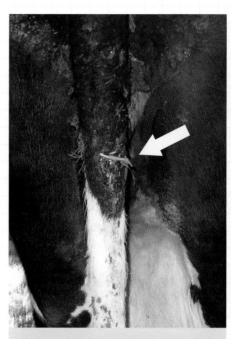

Dried glaze: noticed due to straw stuck on cow's tail at glaze.

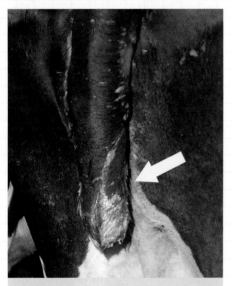

Dried "glaze" on lowest area of tail (docked) should raise suspicion of possible low-grade uterine infection.

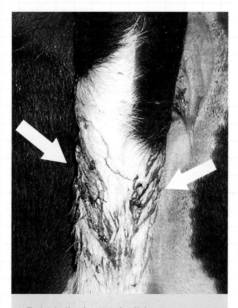

Dried discharge build up indicates uterine infection.

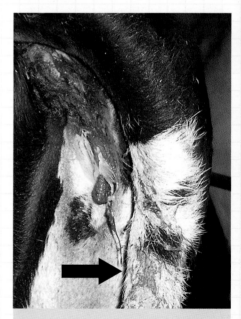

Cow with long standing severe pyometra (a couple gallons of pus in uterus). Surprisingly little discharge on tail — but the dried streaks should raise suspicion. She wasn't coming into heat and the farmer wanted to know why.

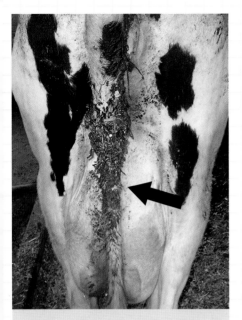

Obvious build-up on tail should raise suspicion about uterine infection.

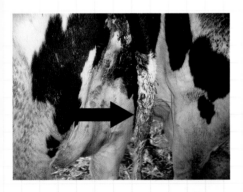

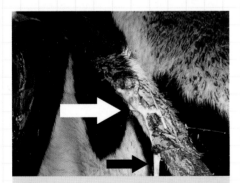

Two pictures of a cow with pus discharge, one month after calving. The picture below clearly shows the pus on the tail head that may be missed without observing closely.

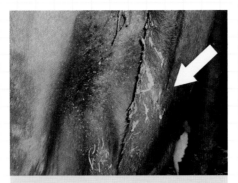

Dried glaze on tail. Black colored tails are more difficult to see contrasts with discharges.

Abnormal Discharge From the Vulva — It is a good thing to inspect tails for any kind of accumulations, *no matter how slight*. Black colored tails are more difficult to see contrasts. Any excess discharge accumulation, other than from being in heat or the first four or five days after calving, should be noted and effectively tended to.

Normal heat discharges are clear. Normal discharge after calving is also clear but a little more straw colored and may have some reddish blood streaks. Anything else is abnormal. Odors are almost always associated with a uterine infection. Infections must be dealt with promptly to prevent chronic infertility.

The *goal* should be that by three or four weeks fresh the uterus needs to be in good condition to breed back. Therefore all uterus problems due to calving (which 95 percent of them are) *must* be effectively treated within 21 days fresh. There is simply no better way to go about things when it comes to organic dairy cows.

Slight Red Streaks Showing on Tail of Cow — A cow that cycles will sometimes show a slight red dis-

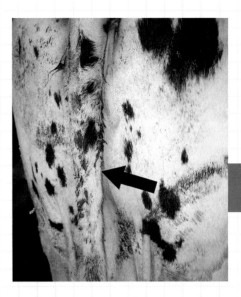

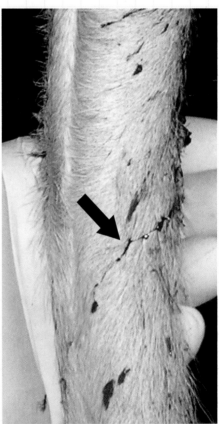

Cow bled off after heat, notice small red streaks.

charge on her tail a few days after heat. This is normal. If the cow was bred on that heat, she still may settle.

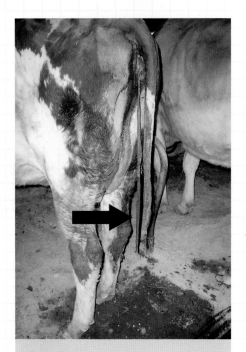

Retained placenta.

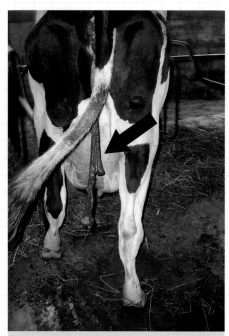

Retained placenta.

Normal clear discharge of a cow in heat.

Retained Placenta — A retained placenta is probably the most common problem after a calving, if there is to be a problem. Retained placentas (*i.e.* the cow didn't "clean" or the cow is "wasting") happen when the afterbirth hasn't yet passed. This usually is a result that there was a hard calving, twins, or she calved in too early. In a cow that had one artificial insemination date and she calved in on that date, it normally takes *five days* for the placenta to decompose enough to pull it out without damaging any structures in the uterus (*i.e.* the caruncles or "buttons").

With a hard calving, twins or an early calving, it will usually take about seven or eight days for the placenta to be pulled out without damaging anything. *Never, ever* "just get some out" a few days after calving — snapping off the placenta

is a terrible thing to do as the rest of it will quickly slide back down into the uterus. Why is this bad? With placenta coming through the cervix, the cervix stays open. When there is no placenta coming through, it will close.

Obviously it is better to have an open cervix to deal with to cleanse a uterus than be shut out from the uterus and having a decomposing placenta stuck in there. This situation unfortunately is common and extremely difficult to deal with on organic farms that cannot use a therapeutic dose of prostaglandins. That is why it is so important to cleanse the uterus *daily* prior to the cervix closing.

Red Discharge From Vulva — In a normal cow that is not bred, a reddish discharge on the tail indicates she went through a heat two or three days previously. Not all cows will show this after heat as many will simply reabsorb this. In a cow that is confirmed pregnant, *a red discharge from the vulva is a definite "red flag."* Something is not right with the pregnancy and she should be checked without delay. She may be about to abort and will possibly need help to extract the fetus.

If she is within a few weeks of calving, she may be calving in early with twins or have some other problem (like a leg or the head is turned back). Letting a cow go on in this situation can spell disaster as the calf will rot inside the cow.

Sometimes, a confirmed pregnant cow showing a red discharge may not even be bred any longer and simply went through a silent heat. In any case, a cow that is confirmed pregnant and showing red discharge *should be checked* as something is occurring and you will want to know what it happening.

RECTAL EXAM

This is actually much better for a veterinarian to do as it is such a common procedure and it certainly becomes an art to be able to figure out what is normal versus abnormal. However, the following sections may at least help you understand what your vet is talking about. The previous section on direct/vaginal exam will be much more valuable for a farmer to understand and refer to since calvings are a normal part of dairy farming.

RUMEN

The rumen, the digestive organ that best characterizes cattle is also the biggest. It generally occupies the left half of the abdomen from top to bottom. It can be felt when the arm is about half way into the cow and a little left of center. It has a "doughy" feeling when pushed upon, much like that of dough being worked to make bread.

Sometimes there will be a big gassy area at its top which is easy to feel while other times it may feel as firm as cement. In some cows off-feed, it will be shrunken due to being somewhat empty. The doughy feel can also be felt by pushing at the triangular area just below the short ribs on the left side of the cow.

KIDNEY

A normal cow kidney has small squares all over it, much like a patchwork quilt design. It is slightly smaller than a grown man's fist and is at the very top of the abdomen under the backbone at about a full arm's length in. Only the back end of one of the kidneys is usually palpable (touchable). If larger than a man's fist, there is probably an infection.

Kidney infections may come from nearly anything affecting the animal systemically as the kidneys are a key filter of blood. But most likely, kidney infections start from an infection in the bladder or after calving when there is an infected uterus. Why? Because there can be a backwards flow of fluid or bacteria from the uterus and/or bladder to the kidneys.

On rare occasion, there will be a crackly, "spongy" feel around the outside of the kidneys. This is found in conjunction with subcutaneous emphysema (air accumulation under the skin). In these cases, the kidneys seem to hang lower in the abdomen.

BLADDER

The bladder is often not detectable and a person not accustomed to reaching into cows will not feel it at all. A firm, small bladder may indicate an infection. A really large "water balloon" size may indicate low calcium if found in an older cow which is just fresh.

UTERUS

The uterus size depends on pregnancy status or days since calving. Interpreting the size of the uterus is an art learned over time by veterinarians and herd managers working with large herds. Examination is usually done via rectal palpation. The uterus should always be freely movable and never stuck in place anywhere. If it is stuck in place this indicates that a localized peritonitis (infection of the abdomen) has occurred, either due to (1) a minor rip during calving, (2) a bad uterine infection from a retained placenta after calving, or (3) an infusion rod being used too aggressively and going through the uterine wall (not uncommon for farmers who infuse on their own but have never been trained how to actually do it).

Swelling of the birth canal, sometimes only in one area but more commonly the entire circumference, indicates a rough calving which will undoubtedly set the animal back, especially if a rip occurred and the abdomen has been infected. An enlarged cervix, usually detected at a standard reproduction examination at about a month fresh indicates that there was a difficult calving.

A cervix which is swollen will not be closed properly and potentially allow material from the outside to enter and create or maintain a uterine infection. (For conditions of the uterus associated with calving, see the *Reproduction & Calving* section.) Treatment for enlarged cervix usually involves waiting a couple months to see if it resolves.

AORTA

The aorta is the largest artery in the body. While reaching in rectally, you might as well feel the aorta to gauge its strength and regularity. Simply turn your palm to the cow's backbone and feel the pulse that is nearby. It should be constant and even. Any variation or "fading" of the pulse force indicates a heart or circulatory condition most likely.

TUMORS

If a tumor is detected anywhere in the abdomen it can mean there are more. However, it is also good to try to differentiate a tumor from an abscess — this can be difficult. However, with a good knowledge of the history of the animal, a more likely diagnosis can be made. This really should be left to a veterinarian — differentiating diseases based upon physical exam findings and animal history are hallmarks of clinical veterinary medicine.

Air Detected in the Abdomen — If it is easy to lightly "slap" organs and structures in the abdomen while doing a rectal examination, this indicates that air is present. *Air is normally never in the abdomen*. A common reason for air in the abdomen occurs after a *standing* surgery for a left-displaced abomasum (LDA), since incising the abdomen will allow a rush of air to come in, get trapped when closing the surgical area, and only slowly be reabsorbed by the animal's system over a couple of weeks time. There will usually be no fever associated with a surgical introduction of air. In this instance, the animal will likely be eating better than prior to the surgery.

A truly pathologic reason is when there is peritonitis (abdominal infection), especially due to a foreign body piercing an organ, and releasing unwelcome air (and other offending material) into the abdomen. These animals will have a fever, usually between 102.9-103.5 F (39.4-39.7 C), in my clinical experience.

Tight Bands, Loops of Bowel — If a veterinarian tells the farmer that an off-feed cow has tight bands detected (mesentery) or loops of bowel easily detectable, this is a cardinal sign of a cow that is gravely ill — if not immediately then as time ticks on over the course of the day. Occasionally, the cow will also be noticed to lower her right hook bone — this is further evidence of a serious gut problem (usually a twisted gut blockage of some kind is happening). If no manure is being passed — *and the rectal sleeve has no manure on it after reaching in* — call for a butcher and salvage the animal for burgers and hot dogs. A cow that is difficult to get to stand and then lies down right away after the physical exam is beyond hope. Emergency salvage in a short time (within an hour) *may* yield usable hamburger or hot dogs but then again it may not – depending on what the butcher finds.

A blocked gut ruins normal circulation of the blood, which provides normal nourishment of cell and whisks away toxins. Any twist of an organ (*i.e.* the gut, the uterus or a right-sided twist) will slowly but surely lead to death if not promptly addresses by effective means. This is why having a good relationship with your local veterinarian is so important.

The Medicine Cabinet

Diagnostics, medicines, administration tools

Materials

- Stomach pump
- Thermometer
- Stethoscope
- Magnets
- IV line (clear is preferred over tan colored)
- Electric prod (better than a pitch fork!)
- Ketone and pH strips
- Calving chains/straps
- Calf tube feeder
- Butane powered dehorner to disbud young calves
- Come-alongs and beam hooks
- Infusion pipettes
- Teat dilators
- Pill gun
- Syringes (3cc, 12cc, 20cc, 35cc, 60cc)
- Needles (14, 18 and 20 gauge, 1-2 inch length)

Medicines

- Phyto-Mast*
- Plasma Gold organic plasma products (IV, IM, SQ injectible) to rapidly enhance health. The closest thing to an antibiotic *without* being an antibiotic.
- Calf oral electrolytes.
- Adult cow injectible electrolytes — calcium borogluconate 23%, CMPK*, Cal-Phos 2*, dextrose, hypertonic saline, lactated ringers solution*, sodium iodide*, etc. The working definition of electrolyte is that any salt dropped into water yields an electrolyte solution.
- Injectible vitamins: A, D, E; vitamin B complex; vitamin B_{12}*; vitamin C*; vitamin E & selenium.
- Phyto-Biotic herbal tincture to enhance health.
- Get Well herbal tablets to enhance health.
- Heat Seek herbal tablets to enhance signs of heat.
- Immunoboost
- MuSe*

- Bio-Vet products to help maximize digestion of feed — RumenAider Paste, Pyck-Me-Up, Generator Elite, Pecti-Cap and Cal-D-Cap (organic variety).
- Biocel CBT injectible colostrum-whey product.
- Utresept for uterine infusion.
- Calcium gel tubes (only calcium chloride allowed, but it is corrosive!)*.
- Laxative boluses — magnesium oxide/magnesium hydroxide ("pink pills").
- Mineral oil or vegetable oil as a *lubricant* for impacted gut.
- Homeopathic remedies.
- Alcohol and alcohol pads.
- Calendula-echinacea ointment.
- Rx materials on 7CFR 205.603* (see appendix at end book for complete listing of allowed synthetic materials for U.S. certified organic livestock health care).
- Epinephrine for allergic reactions.*

* Only available with veterinarian prescription.

For sources of Trade Names mentioned in the Medicine Cabinet see pages 183 & 184.

The Non-Antibiotic Treatment for Infectious Disease

Principles

When not relying on the "silver bullet" approach to treating infections (such as reflexively reaching for an antibiotic), it is imperative to use a variety of approaches to achieve reasonable effectiveness. The following principles are the basis from which I have developed a consistently successful treatment of systemic infectious disease in dairy animals:

1) Biologics to stimulate, augment and/or modulate the immune system.

2) Botanicals with strong antibacterial and healing properties.

3) Antioxidants such as vitamin C and E. Using these first three steps are what I have found to work consistently well to treat *many* kinds of infectious diseases commonly encountered in practice.

4) Fluid Therapy for rehydration is *critical* to restore proper circulatory function. If the circulation is not adequate, any therapy will not work as well. Fluids can be given IV or orally as needed. Truly, any medicine whether antibiotic or homeopathic, will not work well if an animal is showing signs of dehydration and not corrected. Nothing, simply nothing, will work well if the circulation of the animal is slow — this is especially true when considering potential "sludging" taking place in the organs of elimination (liver, kidneys and colon).

5) Antiseptics to cleanse wounds, for wraps to areas needing them and applied internally as needed (uterus and udder).

The Non-Antibiotic Treatment for Infectious Disease

Protocol

While principles are critical to understand, there needs to be materials available at hand to carry out the principles. Based on the above principles and having been engaged in countless battles with infectious disease out in the trenches as a practitioner, the following explicit therapies are what I have developed based on beneficial outcomes in my veterinary practice:

BIOLOGICS

- Plasma Gold or Bovi-Sera for hard quarter with watery secretion, young calf with scours, and any animal with bloody scours and fever. Plasma Gold if breathing issues are involved.

- Plasma Gold
  Adult cow: 250cc IV, follow-up under the skin the next day if needed.
  Calf: 100cc, follow-up under the skin the next day if needed.
- Immunoboost
  Adult cow: 5cc IV/IM/SQ (1cc/200 lbs.)

BOTANICALS

- Phyto-Biotic herbal tincture with garlic, ginseng, goldenseal, wild indigo and barberry.
  Adult cow: 90cc IV loading dose in 500cc dextrose; 15-20cc orally two to three times daily, follow-up for three to four days.
  Calf: 5-10cc orally, two to three times daily.
- Get Well herbal tablets with garlic, ginseng, barberry and Oregon grape.
  Adult cow: four tablets, twice daily for five days.
  Calf: two tablets, twice daily for five days.

ANTIOXIDANTS

- Vitamin C
  Adult cow: 250-500cc IV, one time or 5cc/100lbs. IM once daily for three days (no more than 30cc/site).

ANTISEPTICS

- Hydrogen peroxide, Povidone-iodine scrub (Betadine).

Initial Primary IV Treatment for Adult Cow with Systemic Infection (Has Fever)

1) 250cc Plasma Gold or Bovi-Sera, IV, 5cc Immunoboost, poured into Plasma Gold or Bovi-Sera

2) 90cc Phyto-Biotic orally, poured into 500cc dextrose, IV

3) 250-500cc vitamin C, IV

Follow up with Pyto-Biotic orally, 15-20cc, two to three times daily for three to four days.

Product Descriptions

Phyto-Mast

To Support Udder Health.

Phyto-Mast is a mixture of botanical oils and vitamin E that can be infused into a quarter, only under the direction of the local veterinarian. These are presented in standard white 15cc plastic intramammary infusion tubes, 12/box + alcohol pads. Phyto-Mast is intended to be used as antiseptic irrigation when milk quality is a concern. Phyto-Mast may also be considered for cows that have milk quality concerns at dry off. Any infused quarter should not be put into the bulk tank during the administration period and for eight hours afterward. Animals should not be sold for slaughter during treatment or for three days afterward. Only available through your local veterinarian.

Ingredients: Angelica spp., Mentha sp., Glycyrrhiza sp., Thymus sp. in certified organic canola oil and vitamin E. (all have GRAS status).

Plasma Gold

To Strengthen Vitality.

A highly purified plasma derived from certified organic cows that are immunologically experienced. The closest thing to an antibiotic *without* being an antibiotic. Sterility guaranteed through microbiology quality control laboratory. Source animals are test negative for BLV, BVD and Johne's. Plasma Gold is indicated for times when cows or calves may be experiencing problems commonly encountered. This product is different from other over-the-counter products in that there are no red cells in it, hence it can be considered for IV administration if desired (but always have epinephrine ready). A bottle is either attached to a simplex IV line (250cc bottle) or used as an injection under the skin or in the muscle (100cc or 50cc bottles). Depending on the condition of animal, a bottle can also be given subcutaneously or intramuscularly the next day.

Expiration: thawed & refrigerated — six months; frozen — three years.

Note: Can be thawed and re-frozen a couple times but once the bottle is punctured, use all the contents as there is no preservative in it (good for organics).

Bovi-Sera

For use as an aid in the prevention and treatment of enteric and respiratory conditions caused by the microorganisms: *Arcanobacterium pyogenes, Escherichia coli, Mannheimia haemolytica, Pasteurella multocida, Salmonella typhimurium.* Contains thimerosal and phenol as preservatives. Store at 36 to 45 F (2 to 7 C). Do not freeze. Shake well before use. Use entire contents when first opened. Do not vaccinate within 21 days before slaughter. Anaphylactoid reaction may occur following administration of products of this nature. If noted, administer adrenalin or equivalent. Inject subcutaneously or intramuscularly and repeat according to judgment of user. Administer at 12-24 hour intervals until improvement is noted. It is recommended to limit injections to no more than 10 ml per injection site. Provides immediate and short-term protection lasting 7-21 days for calves: 20-40ml as soon after birth as possible.

Treatment: Calves: 40–100cc; Cattle: 75–150cc.

Phyto-Biotic

To Enhance Health.

A liquid tincture of plants that have well known, strong antibacterial and healing properties. Phyto-Biotic is most often used as an oral treatment (but can be given IV as a loading but needs to be diluted into a carrier such as dextrose or physiologic saline.) Oral dose of Phyto-Biotic is 5cc/calf and 20cc/cow given two to three times daily. When administered with other IV fluids, a 90cc dose is given one time. This is a good adjunct treatment and/or follow-up for animals that received Plasma Gold.

Ingredients: *Allium sativum, Panax ginseng, Hydrastis canadensis, Baptisia tinctoria, Berberis vulgaris,* certified organic alcohol.

Heat Seek

For Reproductive Health.

A botanical blend of herbs that enhances the visually observable signs of estrus. For use in animals that are in normal body condition, have a CL on the ovary, and have not shown visible for long periods of time. Tablets for oral administration: two tablets daily for six days in a row or until heat, whichever is first. Also for cystic ovaries: two tablets daily for 12 days in a row or until heat, whichever is first. Many times estrus will be observed prior to final dose — if so, discontinue administration and breed. Sometimes animals will show heat a few days after the final (sixth) dose. Cows treated with Heat Seek tend to settle well. Occasionally, a cow will show a heat after the final administration of Heat Seek and be bred but then show a flaming heat three weeks later. Breed again. This product is not for cows in negative energy balance.

Ingredients: *Turnera diffusa, Dioscorea villosa, Mitchella repens, Actaea racemosa, Viburnum opulus, Angelica sinensis, Oenothera biennis, Linum usitatissimum,* vitamin B_6, non-GMO yeast.

Get Well

To Enhance Health.

This is a dry, powdered version of the Phyto-Biotic described above. Some farmers prefer to give capsules instead of liquids. Given as a follow-up to a loading dose of Phyto-Biotic. Get Well should be given at a rate of two capsules twice daily for five days.

Ingredients: *Allium sativum, Panax ginseng, Hydrastis canadensis, Baptisia tinctoria, Berberis vulgaris.*

Phyto-Gest

To Enhance Digestion.

A liquid tincture of plants known to stimulate appetite and gut motility. Indications would be mild bloat, constipation, impacted rumen, or potential displaced abomasum. This can be given at the rate of 15-20cc/cow (or horse) or occasionally at 5-10cc IV with a diluent such as dextrose or physiologic saline.

Ingredients: *Gentiana lutea, Zingiber officinale, Nux vomica, Foeniculum vulgare,* certified organic alcohol.

Immunoboost

An immunotherapeutic injection for the treatment of *E. coli* (K99) diarrhea. Calves are born with a complete but immature immune system. Immunoboost stimulates a calf's own immune system to enhance defense mechanisms against disease. Stimulating a non-specific immune response activates macrophages, interleukin production, and both cell mediated immunity and antibody production. "Turning on" the immune system helps a calf respond quickly and get back to normal health faster. A survival rate of 90 percent was demonstrated in an *E. coli* (K99) challenge study with colostrum deprived calves treated once with Immunoboost. No other supportive therapy was administered.

RumenAider Paste (Organic)

RumenAider Paste is a microbial and vitamin supplement designed specifically for cattle, sheep and goats. RumenAider Paste contains over 60 billion CFUs of live microbials per 15 ml feeding. Use whenever the listed nutrients and microbials are desired.

Pyck-Me-Up (Organic)

Pyck-Me-Up is a gluconeogenic fresh cow supplement that provides propionate, selenium yeast, rapidly available calcium, (K) potassium, magnesium, electrolytes and proteinated trace minerals. Mixes with water. Pyck-Me-Up is an ideal drench to add to your fresh cow protocol.

Generator Elite (Organic)

Generator Elite is a microbial supplement for ruminants. Generator Elite provides high levels of microorganisms, including rumen/intestinal origin bacteria, live yeast, digestive enzyme units and yeast cell walls.

Features: nine species live microbials — over 53 billion total CFUs per 0.5 oz. feeding; rumen propionibacteria shown to utilize lactic acid and nitrate; intestinal lactic acid producing bacteria; 45 billion live cell yeast per feeding, shown to produce enzymes and B vitamins and maintain intake during hot weather; 25,000 units digestive enzymes per 0.5 oz. feeding; yeast cell walls.

Pecti-Cap (Organic)

Pecti-Cap is a fiber/electrolyte/vitamin supplement for cattle. Features dietary pectin fiber, yeast cell walls, electrolytes and vitamins to replenish those lost due to dehydration and disrupted gut microflora.

Features: soluble and insoluble fiber (pectins) — important to normalize intestinal consistency; Fructooligosaccharides (inulin) to help beneficial bacteria; cell wall of *Saccharomyces cerevisiae* yeast; electrolytes with sodium, potassium, chloride and bicarbonate to improve water retention and maintain proper body fluid levels; vitamins, especially B vitamins that are crucial to the body's metabolic functions and serve as antioxidants; kelp, a natural source of electrolytes, vitamins and trace minerals.

Cal-D-Cap (Organic)

One feeding of four Cal-D Caps contains 30 grams of calcium, for immediate and sustained delivery. Rapid and slow release calcium in one product. Contains 20,000 IU of vitamin D_3 for proper calcium utilization.

Biocel CBT

Biocel CBT is a sterile, ultra-filtered permeate of whey derived from first and second milking colostrum of older cows which are immunologically experienced. The fats and heavy proteins are removed, leaving a milk-derived "serum" rich in immuno-modulating substances naturally found in colostrum such as antibodies (immunoglobulins), lymphokines, cytokines, lactoferrins, proline-rich polypeptides, lysozymes and numerous other substances that may orchestrate the immune cascade in animals. Biocel CBT is not intended as an adequate source of passive antibodies. Biocel CBT contains a minimum 5 percent crude protein.

MuSe

A source of injectible vitamin E and selenium. Generally needed for geographic areas that are low in soil selenium. Helps to prevent retained placenta. Also as an anti-oxidant. Available only through your local veterinarian (needs veterinary label).

Ecto-Phyte

A safe and effective alternative to noxious and toxic insecticides, used to control flies and external parasites such as lice, fleas and mange. The Ecto-Phyte formulation is based upon the aromatic compounds found in essential oils. These oils are rich in terpenes, aldehydes, cineoles, esters and alcohols and are very antagonistic to both the adult and larval stages of insects. Parasites such as lice which live their entire life cycle, egg through adult, on the animals' hide are immobilized by these aromatic compounds thereby interrupting the pests' cycle and eradicating the problem. The formulation is both oil and water soluble. External parasites such as lice can be easily controlled by spraying livestock thoroughly with a mild to strong dilution with oil (depending on the level of infestation).

Utresept

Utresept is an intra-uterine flush made from natural ingredients using new polysaccharide technology. Utresept has a prolonged residual effect, requires no rinsing and unlike many conventional antiseptics its action is not depleted by contact with organic material. Utresept's anti-microbial power is due to a synergistic action created by a reaction between natural organic acids and natural sugars. When Utresept is introduced into the uterus these natural organic acids and sugars combine with those naturally present in the animal to create a powerful and lasting effect. This gives Utresept its unique physical, chemical and biological properties.

Royal Uterine Capsule

For use during the post-partum period to help maintain normal uterine environment. Essential oils to help maintain normal uterine environment for cow reproductive performance post-calving. Fast acting. Contains a foaming agent to encourage adequate coverage of reproductive tract.

🐄 Putting it all together

By blending the visually observable symptoms, pertinent background information and the hands-on physical examination, a farmer can hopefully determine the animal's situation, immediate needs and follow-up steps. With this in mind, a farmer can better decide if a veterinarian should be called in. The trick is to realize when the vet needs to be called versus being able to handle a situation without the vet.

Note: Being aware of the symptoms and general condition of the animal is much more important than simply naming a disease *i.e.* how does the animal appear versus simply saying "mastitis." *The following headings and what they entail will be used throughout the Cases section that follows.*

Primary Sign: This is the primary observation that gets the farmer's attention.

Since animals cannot talk and tell you what is wrong, you *must* take into consideration the signalment, the onset and history of the visually observable signs and the environment to which the animal is exposed.

Signalment: This refers to the age and breed of the animal as well as how long the cow has been fresh (lactating), or weaned/un-weaned if youngstock or bred/un-bred if growing heifer.

History/Onset: This refers to the length of time that visually observable symptoms have been noticed.

Environment: This refers to the animal's surroundings, bedding, weather and/or primary ration.

Observable Signs: These are the signs associated with the Primary Sign. For instance with clots and flakes observed in the milk, other observable signs may be swelling, redness and tenderness of the quarter.

Physical Exam Findings: This refers to findings from a hands-on examination done to arrive at a picture of the entire animal and any deviations from normal. The physical examination requires the farmer to use the senses of sight, smell, touch and hearing as you handle the animal and check her more closely than with visually observable symptoms. The physical exam may be short if the problem is obvious (such as a cut milk vein) or more in-depth (a slow progression of going off-feed). The trick is to realize which indications are treatable by the farmer and which indications truly require veterinary attention.

When a farmer is not sure if a veterinarian needs to come to the farm, placing a simple phone call relaying a list of symptoms gained from a reasonably thorough physical examination will help immensely. Once you have *as many symptoms as possible,* never hesitate to call your veterinarian to decide if a farm visit should be made or if a vet visit can wait.

Barn Diagnosis: This is the barn-based conclusion made from observations and physical exam findings as to what might be the animal's primary problem. A barn diagnosis based on the signalment, onset/history, environment and physical exam findings leaves open the possibility that there could be something else happening. Indeed, it is true that there may be more than one problem affecting an animal at one time. However, the Barn Diagnosis provides a sound basis for Initial Treatment.

Diagnosis is a key skill learned by people who have graduated from a school of human medicine, veterinary medicine or dental medicine. It literally means "through knowledge." While farmers can observe common symptoms, veterinarians are specially trained to sort out problems when confronted with subtle symptoms derived from physical examination. Veterinarians can come up with a list of rule-outs (differential diagnosis) taking into account the history of the animal and the physical exam findings. For both the farmer and veterinarian, a barn diagnosis is often made simply from the facts as they present themselves for the case at hand.

Veterinarians understand the implications of what they hear through a stethoscope and when reaching into the abdomen via rectal palpation or into the uterus via direct vaginal examination. The farmer should consider as many items as possible when calling the vet.

Certain *cardinal signs* can help guide a farmer regarding treatments. This is why it is important to consider signalment, onset or duration of problem and the environment in order to complete the picture arrived at by physical examination. The more observations a farmer can make, the better the treatment will likely be. Always be aware that there can be subtle signs or vague symptoms not always caught with a quick physical exam. There is no substitute for a complete hands-on examination, either by the farmer or the veterinarian. Immediately after a barn diagnosis is made with organic cattle, treatment should be initiated without delay in order to give the best possible chance of success.

I have often been called on the phone and asked to look at a cow that is "off-feed and has cold ears." If a farmer were to consider the following *additional* points of onset/history, signalment and the cow's temperature: "she is just fresh," "her temperature is 100.0" and "she is fifth lactation" — it is then easy to arrive at a barn diagnosis. Most dairy farmers would immediately know that a logical starting place would be to administer calcium IV for likely low blood levels of calcium (hypocalcemia/milk fever). In most

cases, this would be the correct course of action. However, without checking the cow any closer, any cow that is just fresh with a temperature of 100.0 F (37.8 C) could actually be suffering from a watery quarter or a rip in the uterus from calving.

Initial Treatment: The initial treatment is what should be done based on the signalment, history/onset, environment and physical exam findings. Initial treatment is *not* based on the naming of a disease alone. The initial treatment may include medicine, surgery, manual manipulations (for calving), etc. The initial treatment is to effectively address the problem(s) presently occurring.

In a very real sense, addressing the *symptom picture* is much more important than simply naming a disease and applying a medicine to the named condition. Holistic treatments include looking at the animal's setting (land, ration, housing, bedding, etc.) and taking into account its symptoms and then formulating a plan to best correct the situation, which usually means correcting something in the animal's setting as well as administering natural treatments.

Follow-Up: Follow-up includes any measures needed to be taken to make sure that the initial treatment continues to make a positive impact. Follow-up also may include testing, interpreting the test results and implementing herd management changes (*ex:* milk cultures that show contagious strep ag).

Considerations: Considerations are possibilities that may need to be taken into account if the same symptoms are presented in a slightly different way.

Summary: The readily observable symptoms will be the building blocks from which to form an opinion of what may be wrong and what corrective action would be best — but always try to "color in" the clinical findings with signalment, history/onset, environment *and* physical exam findings.

Having a good relationship with your local veterinarian is *always* preferable to calling a veterinarian from another state that has never been on your farm. If your local veterinarian doesn't know about organics, have your local vet call the out of state organic vet so they can put their medical expertise together to help you better. With the farmer and local veterinarian both involved, farm animals benefit and organic consumers are assured of good cow care.

Farm animal welfare is enhanced when the farmer takes prompt action to correct a specific situation and makes changes to help prevent such situations from arising in the future.

 # Cases

This section is to provide the farmer with real situations that the author has been involved with over the years. Most are real situations that occur commonly as well as some not so commonly found. They are presented to the reader pretty much the same way as they are called in and then examined as a practitioner.

The following sections illustrate how to work through different types of cases. Each case starts with the most obvious sign that the farmer will notice. The goal is to provide straightforward specific treatment (generic approach and trade name products) while respecting USDA certified organic regulations. Consistent positive outcomes have occurred repeatedly with the methods shown.

It should be emphasized that most conditions presented require a multi-prong/holistic approach for its resolution, especially when using natural methods of treatment.

It will be noticed that a certain "routine" set of medicines are used in the cases presented. This is especially true in cases that involve systemic infection (usually reflected by the animal having a fever). Much like dairy farmers who generally have a certain routine in their daily work, veterinarians also have certain routines that are relied upon. In my case, it is using the biologics and botanicals as contrasted by the usual reliance on antibiotics and hormones. While some of the routines may seem repetitive, please know that through a lot of blood, sweat and tears I have winnowed out useless treatments from ones that actually work — across a variety of conditions encountered clinically. Just like other clinicians, I have learned by trial and error, and record here the natural treatments which have helped heal real life cases across many, many farms — in different seasons of the year, under different management capabilities and with different breeds of cows. I just

DRY BEDDING

+ FRESH AIR

+ SUNSHINE

+ WELL-MANAGED PASTURES

+ HIGH FORAGE RATIONS

= HEALTHY ANIMALS

ask for the animals' sake that you start treatments as early as possible when you notice something wrong with an animal under your care. This is the most basic requirement for people who interact closely with animals and who depend on us *entirely* for their well being.

Prevention of almost all diseases involves what I described earlier in this book for healthy organic livestock. Since it can never be repeated enough, here it is again: dry bedding + fresh air + sunshine + well-managed pastures + high forage rations = healthy animals. As stated earlier in the book, try to mimic mother nature as closely as possible and you will have dramatically fewer problems. For example, calves on nurse cows will be the healthiest and quickest growing calves. If not using nurse cows, feed whole milk for a minimum of three months in order to have very healthy, hefty calves prior to weaning so they can better deal with the stresses that come afterwards.

Yet, as with anything to do with livestock, odd things can happen, even with proper prevention.

Flakes & Clots in Milk

Signalment: Sixth lactation Holstein, fresh six months, bred two months, eating fine.

History/Onset: Mastitis flakes come and go, has had high SCC.

Environment: Hot humid weather, late in summer. Likely heat stress.

Observable Signs: Flakes and stringy mastitis.

Physical Exam Findings: Clots and very high SCC on CMT plate; nothing remarkable except a slightly swollen quarter. Friendly, big, blocky cow, doesn't mind being worked on.

Barn Diagnosis: Clinical mastitis.

Initial Treatment: Should culture the milk to identify which bug may be associated with mastitis. Phyto-Mast antiseptic tubes in quarter for four to six milkings in a row.

Follow-up: Depends on milk culture. Consider culling if other problems exist with cow; if Staph aureus, milk cow last to not pass on the infection to other cows or make the cow a nurse cow. If environmental strep dysgalactiea, strep uberis, staph epidermidis, etc., check milking hygiene and technique. Phyto-Mast has worked nicely on simple environmental mastitis.

Considerations: Homeopathic constitutional prescribing — Calc Carb, immune stimulation with ginseng — 4 grams daily for at least six days in a row.

Milk Looks Normal But Very High in Somatic Cell Count (SCC)

Signalment: Fourth lactation Jersey, fresh three months. Brought into herd from herd dispersal last lactation.

History/Onset: Very high SCC shortly after arrival into herd (at first DHIA test). Previous owner was not on any milk testing program.

Environment: Ground peanut hulls for bedding; pleasant and comfortable spring weather.

Observable Signs: None really, milk looks OK. Cow comes up very high on SCC as shown by monthly milk testing. SCC of about 2,000,000. CMT paddle identifies the LH quarter (gels when mixing purple fluid to milk) to be high in SCC with the RF, RH and LF quarters to be normal.

Physical Exam Findings: Nothing remarkable, eating well, milking well.

Barn Diagnosis: Sub-clinical mastitis, chronic.

Initial Treatment: Immune stimulation with 5cc Immunoboost under skin or 35cc Biocel CBT under the skin daily for three days. Then, three days later infuse an antiseptic into the affected glands with an essential oil product (Phyto-Mast tube in quarter for six milkings in a row). Use a quarter milker to keep the bad quarter out of the tank during treatment and until such time that the CMT paddle shows negative or makes a significant decrease.

CMT plate — the left hind quarter is thicker looking and has a darker color, however the right hind quarter is also bad, though less so. By holding the plate under the cow so the handle is in the direction of the tail, you will always know which quarter is which.

Follow-up: Oral ginseng 4 grams daily for at least six days in a row.

Considerations: Depends on milk culture. Strep ag is likely (very high SCC and normal looking milk). Milk last or separately or make into a nurse cow. For cows with high SCC at dry off, use Phyto-Mast tubes.

PROBLEM: UDDER

Drying-Off with High SCC

Signalment: Cow at end of lactation, any breed.

History/Onset: The SCC has slowly been rising over the last couple months.

Environmental: Anytime, anywhere, but maybe more prevalent during hotter months.

Visually Observable Signs: A flake or two has been seen recently in two quarters.

Physical Exam Findings: Nothing remarkable except for the udder being a bit questionable to dry off.

Barn Diagnosis: Sub-clinical mastitis.

Initial Treatment: Do a CMT test to identify which quarters are having trouble. If possible, get a culture taken prior to dry-off. This will help to see what bug may be present and make management changes if needed. If no flakes and high SCC (above linear SCC 5), use 5cc Immunoboost. If any flakes are seen, give the 5cc Immunoboost and then infuse Phyto-Mast into flaky quarter(s) at each milking for four to six milkings in a row.

Follow-up: Do not milk the cow for five days (to biologically stop the production of milk) and then check the quarters. If no flakes and no udder inflammation, use a tube of Phyto-Mast in each quarter for final dry off. Monitor the cow for the next two weeks as the natural plug forms in the teat end.

Considerations: Many cows will naturally increase in SCC as they get to the tail end of lactation. If a cow is at linear SCC of 4 or less, no dry off treatment is really necessary — just good monitoring and clean environment. If the SCC has crept up or gone up dramatically in the last month or two, follow directions for this case. Some researchers advocate dipping a dry cow's teats twice daily for the first two weeks dry and also during the two weeks right before calving as the natural teat plug is not as functional during those times. However, stimulation of any kind at the teats might induce some animals to want to make milk. Consider vaccination with any of the gram negative/coliform type vaccines (J-5, J-Vac, Endovac-Bovi). Don't do this right at dry off as the immune system takes a mild dip with the stress of a changing routine. Instead vaccinate a week prior to dry off. Follow manufacturer's directions.

Clinical studies have shown that Phyto-Mast significantly reduced the number of new infections during the dry period, so using Phyto-Mast for dry-off is a rational practice, especially for cows with high SCC.

PROBLEM: UDDER

Watery Secretion From Quarter

Signalment: First lactation Holstein, just fresh two days ago.

History/Onset: Within last 12 hours.

Environmental: Middle of summer during heat wave (100 F (39 C); 95 percent humidity).

Visually Observable Signs: Watery secretion from right hind quarter, off-feed.

Physical Exam Findings: Hard, swollen, painful, hot right hind quarter, 104 F (40 C) temperature, dehydrated (by eyebrow pinch test), increased heart rate, lungs OK, uterus OK.

Barn Diagnosis: Coliform mastitis.

Initial Treatment: Dextrose with 90cc Phyto-Biotic tincture (garlic-based tincture), 250cc Plasma Gold or Bovi-Sera (hyperimmune serum), 5cc Immunoboost (immune stimulant), 500cc vitamin C (antioxidant), 1-liter hypertonic saline IV (to stimulate drinking), peppermint essential oil lotion rubbed into quarter topically (for one to two days).

Follow-up: Strip out quarter frequently, reapply peppermint lotion after each stripping, and four tablets Get Well orally (antibacterial botanical boluses) twice daily for four days.

Considerations: Homeopathic Belladonna hourly and Pyrogen four times daily; flunixin IV against pain, swelling and fever (especially if pregnant).

PROBLEM: UDDER

Large, Well-Defined Swelling on One Quarter

Signalment: Fourth lactation cow, fresh about five months.

History/Onset: The swelling on the back of the right hind quarter has increased in size over the last few months. Her somatic cell count has also been slowly rising.

Environment: Any season, any barn, usually older cows.

Observable Signs: The obvious swelling on back side of quarter.

Physical Exam Findings: High somatic cell count (SCC) with CMT paddle of quarter with swelling. On reaching in rectally, the iliac lymph node is larger than normal, otherwise everything else is normal.

Barn Diagnosis: Udder, most likely abscess due to staph aureus or arcanobacter.

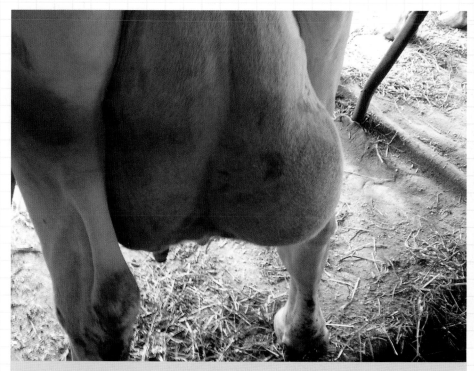

Abscess within quarter, usually indicates a staph aureus infection though not always. If these open up, somatic cell count (SCC) will decrease noticeably.

Initial Treatment: Effective intra-mammary antiseptics (Phyto-Mast) or hyperimmune plasma (Plasma Gold or Bovi-Sera) infused into quarter. Homeopathic low potency Hepar Sulph to help the abscess open up and drain.

Follow-up: Monitor.

Considerations: If the abscess opens up, be happy. The somatic cell count will usually drop if the abscess opens up. Do *not* purposely try to open the abscess as there are many, many blood vessels near the surface of the udder.

PROBLEM: UDDER

Quarter Has Hardly Any Milk, But What it Does Have is Constantly Bad

Signalment: Any lactating cow, but usually one not in the first lactation.

History/Onset: At some point mastitis occurred and for whatever reason was not effectively cured.

Environment: Any.

Observable Signs: Very poor quality milk with clots and flakes. However, not much is being produced — perhaps 20-40 manual strips at each milking.

Physical Exam Findings: No significant findings. Cow is otherwise completely healthy.

Barn Diagnosis: Chronic mastitis. If not cultured, consider culturing to have more information about what kind of mastitis is present. This will help with possible management decisions for the cow or the rest of the herd.

Initial Treatment: Consider killing the quarter. This can be done by infusing either Betadine into quarter for four milkings in a row without stripping out the quarter in between. However, if Betadine is used, flunixin will be needed since an inflammation will occur in the gland. Otherwise, chlorhexidine (Nolvasan solution) can be used. I prefer the chlorhexidine method as inflammation doesn't occur. Chlorhexidine is allowed on organic farms as an alternative teat dip and for surgical purposes. I believe that the use of chlorhexidine in the man-

ner described fits the organic use allowance. Use 60cc chlorhexidine in quarter for four milkings in a row *without stripping out.*

Follow-up: Hold out milk from tank for all four quarters while doing this procedure and for 96 hours afterwards.

Considerations: Killing a quarter is best done when there is hardly any milk quantity being expressed from teat. In other words, the quarter seems to want "to die" but just won't and you are helping it along. This procedure does not work well on fresh cows that are producing a lot of milk from the gland in question.

PROBLEM: UDDER

Dry Cow is Sluggish, has Swollen Udder

Signalment: Third lactation Holstein, pregnant eight months and dry.

History/Onset: Not totally sure since she was outside with other dry cows for the last few weeks and the farmer has been busy with the harvest.

Environmental: Nice weather in October; had a lot of flies clinging to cows recently.

Visually Observable Signs: Swollen quarter, walks a bit slowly, seems "droopy," dry manure, and eats only a little bit when brought into barn.

Physical Exam Findings: Temperature of 105 F (41 C), dehydrated on eyebrow pinch test, pudding secretion from swollen quarter *with foul odor,* still pregnant (bumped calf*), heart rate 90 beats per minute, lungs a bit raspy, rumen slow but functioning.

Barn Diagnosis: Arcanobacter mastitis (probably due to flies on teat ends).

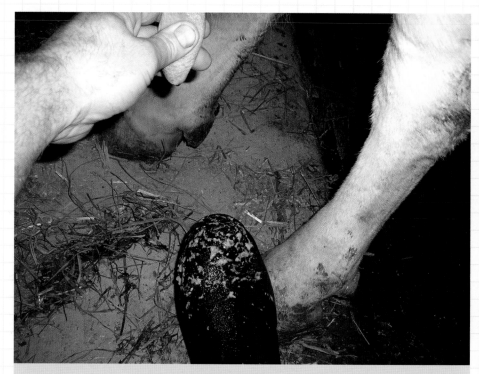

Clots in milk indicate mastitis. Always keep such quarters out of bulk tank. Consider a quarter milker. This cow's discharge had an obviously foul odor. There is only one kind of mastitis like that — arcanobacter.

Initial Treatment: Flunixin IV to drop fever since pregnant; IV 500cc Dextrose with 90cc Phyto-Biotic (garlic-based tincture), 250cc Plasma Gold or Bovi-Sera (hyperimmune plasma), 5cc Immunoboost (immune stimulant), 500cc vitamin C (antioxidant), 1-liter hypertonic saline IV (to stimulate drinking), peppermint essential oil lotion rubbed into quarter topically (for one or two days).

Follow-up: Strip out quarter frequently, re-apply peppermint lotion after each stripping, and four tablets Get Well orally (antibacterial botanical boluses) twice daily for four days.

Considerations: Homeopathic Belladonna hourly and pyrogen four times daily; flunixin IV against pain, swelling and fever. Quarter will never be functional again. Penicillin will be effective for systemic Arcanobacter infections; it is given at 25cc in muscle twice daily for five days. These cases sometimes turn into gangrene. Be careful.

---

*"Bumping a calf" is when the actual calf can be felt when repeatedly pushing in and out at the lower right abdomen. The calf is detectable only at about six-and-a-half months or more of pregnancy.

PROBLEM: UDDER

Gas from Quarter When Stripped Out

Signalment: Third lactation Holstein-Normande, fresh three days ago, not eating a thing.

History/Onset: Within last two hours.

Environment: In the stable, soft wood shavings for bedding, tie-stall barn.

Observable Signs: Swollen right front quarter, no milk — only gas expressed when stripped.

Physical Exam Findings: Bright and alert, temperature is 107 F (42 C), hydration OK (eyebrow pinch test), right front quarter hot and hard.

Barn Diagnosis: Likely gangrene setting in (early).

Initial Treatment: IV 500cc dextrose with 90cc Phyto-Biotic (garlic based tincture), 500cc vitamin C, 250cc Plasma Gold or Bovi-Sera (hyperimmune plasma). Use hydrogen peroxide in the quarter — 60cc of 3% strength. Strip out in five minutes. Repeat again. One of the germs that cause gas gangrene thrives in a low to no oxygen environment — hydrogen peroxide gives a blast of oxygen to the area to make the environment less friendly to the germs.

Follow-up: 15-20cc Phyto-Biotic (garlic-based tincture), three times daily for four days. If quarter becomes cold and bluish with gas, cut teat off to allow release of toxic gases. Possibly use an essential oil infusion tube for the quarter (Phyto-Mast).

Considerations: High possibility of gangrene developing — strongly consider penicillin. There are two types of gas gangrene: Staph aureus ("blue bag") and clostridium. If high fever and bright and alert (likely staph aureus type), immune system is activated and can perhaps still be augmented. If cow is standing with low fever, depressed and dehydrated (likely clostridium type) with gas from quarter, go to penicillin immediately. If cow is down, depressed with gas quarter and grunting with each breath — too late, she will probably die within a few hours.

Down cow with watery secretion; turned out to be gangrene when gas was stripped out shortly after picture was taken. The teat was very cool to touch and "flabby" feeling.

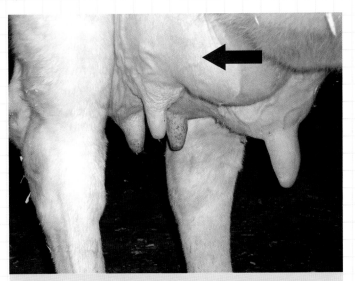

Three quartered cow recovered from gangrene mastitis, using the non-antibiotic treatment of infectious disease (no antibiotics). Three quartered cows can be found on organic and conventional farms.

PROBLEM: UDDER

Small Puddles of Blood Underneath Cow

Signalment: Usually an older cow, lactating.

History/Onset: Cow has a large udder with high udder attachment that swings from side to side as she walks to pasture. She has prominent milk veins and veins on the side of her udder. For a few days, blood has been on the ground after she rises. Farmer tried to determine where it was coming from but couldn't.

Environment: Poorly managed pasture in an old field with old fence material along perimeter. Stalky stubble from rank weed growth.

Observable Signs: Spots or areas of blood underneath her.

Physical Exam Findings: Cow is perhaps a little weak, but still stands quite well. Dried on dirt along the milk veins make it difficult to see where the probable cut is located. Vulva membranes are pale pink (not white but also not a normal pink).

Barn Diagnosis: Likely laceration of the milk vein (or udder vein) with possible significant blood loss. Call veterinarian immediately.

Note: To quick stop a cut on a milk vein (or even an udder), use a clothespin from the wash line and clamp it off until the vet can come.

Initial Treatment: The vet will cleanse the milk veins well to find the cut. It most likely is there somewhere. However, don't forget to check surface veins on the udder. Be ready for the vet to stitch the moment the cut is located because it is likely that a lot of blood will start spurting once the dried cake of dirt is removed. Stitch with PDS size 2. It usually only takes one or two stitches at most. Putting in more stitches may create more bleeding.

Follow-up: Fluids IV will help (and are really needed) if it is thought that a lot of blood has been lost in a short time. This can be assessed by looking at the eye socket or vulva membranes to see how pink vs. white they are. Three to four liters of lactated ringers solution and a bottle of dextrose will help most cows. Consider calcium (especially if older cow) since this mineral is directly tied to the blood clotting mechanism and with a severe loss of blood, clotting abilities are negatively impacted.

Considerations: Cows that have lost a lot of blood in a short time may not stand up for long. This should be a tip off that they need fluids IV to expand the blood volume or a blood transfusion. A cow that is down with a known milk vein cut and is breathing shallowly and quickly is a very weak animal due to the blood loss. For some of these it is too late but they need a transfusion without doubt if the area can be stitched in time.

BLOOD TRANSFUSIONS

Here is the method I use, which I think is probably the quickest and easiest. Find a friendly cow that is nearly dry — if she is related to the recipient cow all the better, but don't worry if she isn't. Sedate her slightly with xylazine and/ or butorphanol, have someone tail-jack the cow, then insert a 14 or 12 gauge needle into the milk vein, ready to catch the blood into an extremely clean liter size bottle to which sodium citrate or heparin (a biologic) is added as an anticoagulant. Better yet is to do the milk vein on each side. Constantly swirl the bottle as you catch the blood draining out of the needle. Once the bottle is filled (it'll get bubbly near the top), quick go to the recipient cow (constantly swirling the bottle) and run the donor blood in through a standard IV line. Run it in as fast as you can by holding the bottle high and constantly swirling it. Blood transfusions can work miracles for an animal with an obvious cut that has lost a lot of blood and the cut has been stitched. It takes about five minutes to fill a 1-liter bottle. Giving two liters is usually appropriate. You can also give a bottle of dextrose and a few liters of lactated ringers solution. The recipient cow should be brighter by the end of the procedure and normal by the next day if all went well.

PROBLEM: UDDER

Teat End is Damaged

Signalment: Third lactation Holstein fresh six months, bred back (pregnant three months).

History/Onset: Yesterday.

Environment: Tie-stall.

Observable Signs: Teat end is damaged, won't milk out correctly, painful and kicks when milked.

Physical Exam Findings: Hot, hard quarter with white milk and clots.

Barn Diagnosis: Stepped on teat.

Initial Treatment: Sedate cow (or she may kick at your head) and have vet open teat with a surgical instrument to allow milk out. Do this early in the day. Infuse an essential oil antiseptic tube (Phyto-Mast) into the teat immediately after opening the teat since bacteria may have entered during the procedure. Give something to reduce fever — flunixin, aspirin, homeopathic belladonna or pyrogen.

Follow-up: Strip out quarter every 15-30 minutes on day that vet opened up teat. After the first day of frequent stripping out, apply a healing ointment (calendula-echinacea is excellent) and protect the teat end from dirt. Therefore apply a bandage (a short length of hoof wrap will do) that is snug so it won't fall off but not be too tight.

Considerations: If cow is not pregnant and a fever is present, maybe let the fever continue if the cow is still eating since a fever does indicate that the animal is rallying to overcome the challenge. If not eating, then try to lower the fever to get her eating again. If stepped on teats are a problem in a tie-stall barn, the cows are too big for the stalls. Treating a tramped teat by putting dilators into the teat at every milking is usually a recipe for disastrous mastitis — it is simply not possible to keep everything clean every time and at some point bacteria will gain entry into the teat end.

PROBLEM: UDDER

Milks Well But All of a Sudden the Milk Will Stop Flowing

Signalment: Usually a cow that has lactated previously, anytime during lactation.

History/Onset: Farmer notices the quarter is not milked out when taking machine off, can strip out normal milk, but then all of a sudden it stops. Upon continued hand stripping, the milk becomes blocked again and again.

Environment: Anywhere, anytime.

Observable Signs: As described in the history/onset.

Physical Exam Findings: Nothing remarkable, just the presenting symptom.

Barn Diagnosis: Teat floater, teat "spider," teat "pea."

Initial Treatment: Have someone jack up the tail of the cow, then strip out until the blockage occurs; while keeping the blockage right where it is (at the teat opening), clamp off the top of the teat where it attaches to the udder with your other hand, then with "gentle firmness" work the teat pea out of the teat end. This will take effort to work out as well as not having the teat pea slip away upwards (you'll have to start over). A dry teat and hand work better than a moist teat and hand.

Follow-up: None, the problem is finished.

Considerations: Occasionally with a touchy cow a little sedation (xylazine) may be needed.

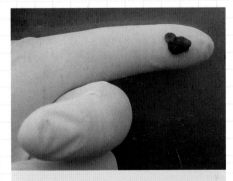

Floater expressed from teat. No cutting of teat needed. Consider the size in relation to the index finger (approximate size and shape of a teat) and the size of a teat opening.

PROBLEM: UDDER

Milk Coming Out From Side of Teat

Signalment: Sixth lactation Brown Swiss cow fresh one month.

History/Onset: Overnight, since last milking.

Environment: Tie-stall, wood shavings for beddings. Kind of large cow for stall.

Observable Signs: Milk comes out of side of teat when prepped for milking.

Physical Exam Findings: Cow guards the quarter and kicks when touched, otherwise no significant findings.

Barn Diagnosis: Laceration of milk canal of teat. Call veterinarian.

Initial Treatment: The vet will lightly sedate cow with 0.2-0.3cc xylazine +/- 1cc butorphanol, infiltrate area to be stitched with lidocaine and then insert an aseptic milk tube to avoid stitching canal shut. The vet will then stitch with Vicryl size 1 for inner layer if needed then Vicryl size 1 or PDS size 2 for skin. Afterwards, infuse one tube of Phyto-Mast after stitching since bacteria may have gotten in prior to noticing the problem.

Follow-up: DMSO — medical grade should be applied by veterinarian at the time of stitching to reduce inflammation. Calendula-echinacea-hypericum (CEH) ointment helps heal the stitched area. Keep the area clean and covered. Can machine milk. Avoid milk drains to minimize mastitis.

Considerations: *This situation needs prompt attention.* Stitches need to be placed within 6-12 hours of occurrence, otherwise too much inflammation occurs and stitching will not work. If dealing with this a few days after it happened, it is too late. Milk will then always come out where there is the path of least resistance. At milking time when the cow lets her milk down, instead of the normal teat end sphincter holding in the milk like usual until milking begins, the milk will come gushing out of the sliced open teat. There would be the possibility of stitching the teat when the cow is dried off, no milk production is happening, and no inflammation is occurring.

Udder Sores

Signalment: Oftentimes a first calf heifer, but not always.

History/Onset: Usually this is detected soon after freshening and the odor made from it can be mistaken for a cow that did not pass her placenta.

Environment: Anytime, anywhere.

Observable Signs: The udder is almost always very enlarged and edematous (caked), making it difficult to walk normally (especially for first calf heifers). In older cows, the udder sore is more likely in between the right and left half of the udder. In heifers it is often between the leg and the udder.

Physical Exam Findings: Normal other than the ulcer occurring in the "armpit" between the udder and leg or centrally between the udder halves.

Barn Diagnosis: Udder sore.

Initial Treatment: It is extremely important to *vigorously* cleanse these areas and make them bleed a little to bring new circulation to the area. I will also use a clipper to clip all the hair at the periphery prior to cleansing (for the centrally located ones). With vigorous scrubbing with an antiseptic of your choice, you will likely see deep crevices or lines — these are the areas that harbor the germs that are associated with this condition (they are related to the

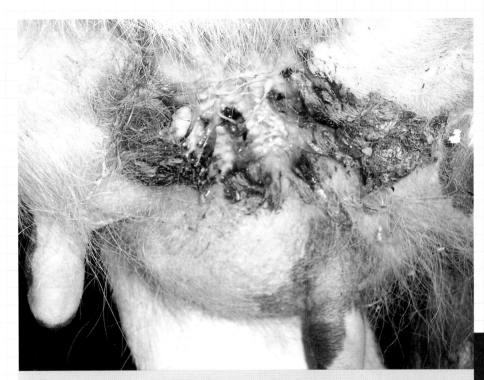

Udder sore. Clip area, scrub vigorously with Betadine and or chlorhexidine, then apply a drying powder. Never apply a salve to these areas as it will trap in germs that like low oxygen conditions.

germs that cause foot rot). They like low oxygen settings. Thus aeration with hydrogen peroxide and drying are the main strategies. Do *not* apply salves or ointments (though it is tempting), as they will create a low oxygen environment. Once cleansed, use a drying powder like cornstarch or the like. Since these are almost always caused by excessive udder swelling (especially in first calf heifers), you need to reduce the size of the udder.

Follow-up: Keep applying a drying powder to the area. Reduce udder swelling as quickly as you can. Homeopathic Merc Cor is very specific to this symptom picture. Graphitis may also be indicated. Use either one, 30C three to four times daily as needed.

Considerations: Preventing large accumulations of fluid in the udder is a primary goal, thus be very careful of the amount of salt springing heifers are allowed to ingest. Use salt blocks versus free choice salts. Also, consider pre-milking an excessively large udder to reduce its size. The quality of colostrum may be affected a little, but colostrum will still occur after the act of calving, regardless of pre-milking. Occasionally, an older cow with a deep, centrally located udder sore may experience it eroding to such an extent that a blood vessel is ruptured. This is really bad as these vessels are extremely difficult to ligate (tie off) and stop bleeding. Applying cayenne pepper or lots of spider webs may help stop the bleeding.

PROBLEM: UDDER

Sloughing Skin on Hind Side of Udder of Fresh Cow

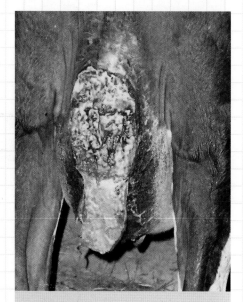

Udder as shown by farmer during routine herd check

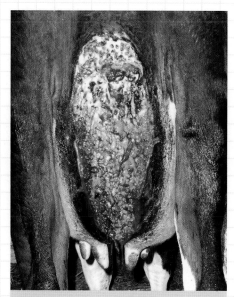

Area of dried skin flap snipped off. Pooled fluid poured out and revealed further udder involvement.

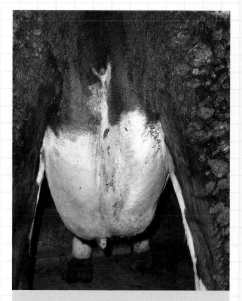

Udder at about four to six months later; farmer had cleaned the area well with Betadine (povidone-iodine) after the dried skin was snipped off. Healed nicely.

Signalment: Second calf Holstein, fresh four weeks.

History/Onset: Had a very enlarged udder and quite firm at freshening for an extended period of time. Clear liquid droplets were seen to be seeping out of the udder early on.

Environment: Any season, tie-stall operation.

Observable Signs: Obvious problem when viewed from rear; dried skin looked suspicious.

Physical Exam Findings: Cow was doing fine and so the focus was only on the local area of the udder.

Barn Diagnosis: Sloughing of skin secondary to extreme udder edema (caking).

Initial Treatment: Snip dry skin off to see the extent of the problem. Cleanse area with soft iodine (Povidone-iodine) for a few days. Allow "tincture of time" to help heal.

Follow-up: None needed, as long as the animal is performing well otherwise.

Considerations: With severe udder edema (caking), gangrene is possible due to very impaired circulation (especially in a dry cow with a rock hard quarter which isn't tended to quickly enough). Plant materials that have diuretic effects should be employed (coffee, juniper, dandelion, etc.) or revert to furosemide (pharmaceutical diuretic).

PROBLEM: UDDER

Fluid Accumulation Within Udder & Under Belly in Front of Udder of Fresh Heifer

Signalment: Just fresh heifer.

History/Onset: The farmer noticed this animal retaining more and more fluid near the udder the last few weeks.

Environment: A group of heifers had been apart from the rest of the herd and had free access to salts of various kinds (free choice mineral systems need to be minimized with springing heifers as most of the minerals are in some sort of salt combination).

Observable Signs: Obvious.

Physical Exam Findings: Other than the uncomfortable feeling of the huge udder between the legs when walking, the heifer seems OK. Pushing into the udder with the index finger leaves a visible depression afterwards.

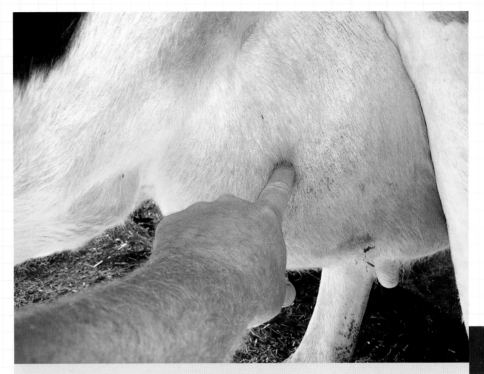

Edema as shown by pushing a finger into the area and seeing if an indentation remains afterwards. Udder edema is most common in freshening heifers; it can be severe and lead to very poor circulation and possibly gangrene in extreme cases.

Barn Diagnosis: Udder edema (caking).

Initial Treatment: Use any kind of diuretic available so the animal will excrete the excess fluids. Coffee (*not* decaffeinated) is an excellent diuretic and can be given right out of the tin and placed into capsules. Give four to six capsules twice a day. Juniper is also a good herbal diuretic. Furosemide is an injectible diuretic that works quite well but may cause loss of excess potassium from the system. It is given at the rate of 10cc in the muscle twice daily for a few days. Homeopathic Apis Mel 30C two to three times daily may be of added benefit.

Follow-up: As above.

Considerations: Pre-milking animals may be of value in those whose udders are becoming very filled up. Restrict free access to salt in springing animals but especially springing heifers.

PROBLEM: UDDER

Leathery, Darkened Teats of Fresh Heifer

Signalment: First calf heifer, fresh 10 days.

History/Onset: Heifer had some udder and belly edema (caking) prior to calving.

Environment: Cold weather, wintertime in northern climate.

Observable Signs: One or more teats have become "leathery" and difficult to milk, causing mastitis to develop.

Physical Exam Findings: Nothing out of the ordinary except for the obvious damage of the teats' skin.

Barn Diagnosis: Herpes mammalitis.

Initial Treatment: No treatment will really help that well. The best route is to use an emollient salve. An ideal one would contain calendula, echinacea and hypericum in a lanolin base. Unfortunately, these quarters almost always become mastitic. They become hard to milk

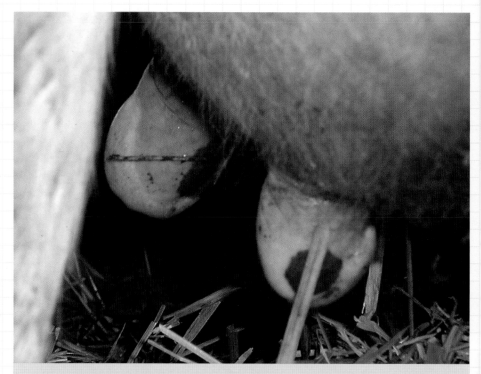

Blisters on teats — early herpes mammillitis. This stage is rarely observed. Usually only the "leathery" teats are noticed when milking.

and there is a desire to open the teat canal with an instrument. This will likely cause more harm than good (in this situation) by bringing germs from the bad teat skin into the milk canal.

Follow-up: Liberal application of salves to keep area as soft as possible.

Considerations: Herpes mammillitis is caused by a virus. It seems to be most damaging to udders that are swollen with poor general cir-

culation (like a springing first calf heifer) and especially in the wintertime. There may be advantage to using the equine flu vaccine as a preventive or perhaps the homeopathic nosode if caught very early. Homeopathic *Urtica Urens* may be indicated, as the feel of warmth is welcomed in these cases (versus Apis Mel which is indicated when coolness is applied to an area). Since this condition almost always happens in wintertime, applications of cool would be contra-indicated.

PROBLEM: EATING & FEED

Slow to Eat, Fresh a Couple of Days

Signalment: Fourth calf Holstein, fresh five days.

History/Onset: Hasn't been doing well since calving, does eat but according to the farmer "not the way she should."

Environment: Tie-stall, late winter, not yet grazing. Ration consists of hay, baleage, some grain and minerals.

Observable Signs: Cow finishes feed but slowly, there is some slight *muscle twitching* at the shoulder blades and some, but even less, at the rear leg flanks. Manure is normal, possibly a little on the firm side.

Physical Exam Findings: Cow has cool ears and is cool to touch along the backbone, temperature is 100.3 F (38 C), rumen is slow and has a slight gas cap which can be heard with a stethoscope and can be seen as a very slight bloated look. Kidneys are normal, uterus is normal. Urine is slightly positive for ketosis. No pings are heard on the left or right sides. Udder is soft, no positive CMT. A very slight positive eyebrow pinch test. Pupils contract a bit slowly when a light is shined into them.

Barn Diagnosis: Low blood calcium with slightly low blood sugar (ketosis).

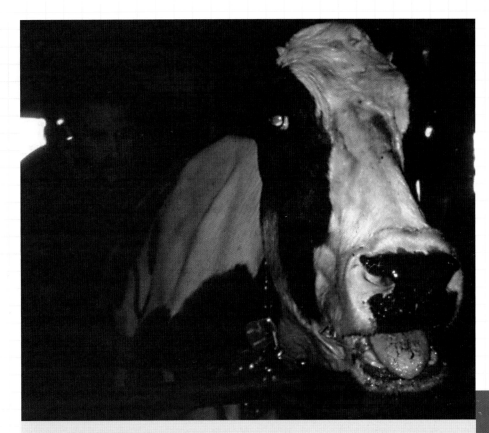

Pulling up on the skin of a standing fresh cow's back and her response is opening her mouth: likely low calcium.

Initial Treatment: IV calcium product — *hold bottle no higher than her backbone* — can give a bottle of dextrose as well. Add in vitamin B complex or vitamin B12. Most IV calcium products have some form of sugar in them as well (dextrose, glucose).

Follow-up: Calcium product orally. Exercise. Feed her anything she will eat. Add some molasses on top of feed to sweeten it up. Could pump the stomach with 5-gallons water to which Pyck-Me-Up (Organic) and Generator Elite is added. If not pumping the stomach, RumenAider (Organic) and Cal-D Cap (Organic) should be used.

Considerations: A cow that is slightly low in calcium (after all she *is* still standing up) and slightly ketotic can set up to become a twisted stomach (displaced abomasum — DA). Be careful not to feed too much grain and not enough hay to these kinds of cows as fermentation of the grain may occur in the abomasum and push them over into a DA.

Note: Admittedly, the condition of being fresh and slow to eat is very common on commercial dairies. Truly, a full physical examination is needed to either rule out common causes of problems and/or to definitively identify the root cause.

Eats Very Little & Won't Touch Her Grain

Signalment: Third lactation, Holstein, fresh one to two weeks.

History/Onset: Cow was doing fine until about four days ago when she started to back off of her feed. She has been given calcium IV two times, the latest being a couple days ago.

Environment: Springtime early grazing in a herd that has a strong spring flush (most cows becoming fresh in March through April). Cool spring weather with green grass in pasture but slow growth due to cloudy days. Cows are in a bedded pack housing system and parlor milking.

Observable Signs: She walks kind of wobbly and seems a bit "sleepy." Breath smells like acetone or glue. She likes molasses.

Physical Exam Findings: Cold ears, temperature is normal, heart and lungs are normal, rumen is slow, ping on the left, no ping on the right, manure is diarrhea-like, and udder is soft. Urine test strip shows immediate purple color on ketone pad. No other significant findings.

Barn Diagnosis: Left-sided twisted stomach (displaced abomasum LDA) with concurrent secondary ketosis.

Correct position of rope to pull a cow down (cow also has halter on and is temporarily tied to a post). A 35-foot length of rope is needed. This procedure will take two people to carry out. If correcting a left-sided displaced abomasum by this method, free the cow's head from the post (but have someone hold the halter up front); the other person stands behind the cow and pulls on the rope. From the back position, have the cow fall clockwise, then take her legs and roll her clockwise over on her back, and then stand her up. Listen for the ping that was on the left side. It should not be there. Get her moving around and make sure she is freely moving around the next couple days.

Initial Treatment: IV dextrose either before or after surgery to correct the problem.

Follow-up: The twisted stomach must be addressed, otherwise the cow will not start eating again, the ketosis will continue, and she will decline further. Decide upon surgery to correct the twisted stomach or possibly *roll the cow* to correct the twisted stomach (see photo). If trying to correct the situation without surgery, the principle to work from is: get the gut moving by all means possible. This could include calcium for muscle strength of the digestive tract, laxatives like aloe, magnesium hydroxide, Epsom salts, "pink pills," etc. Can also try RumenAider and Generator Elite. Make sure the animal is *not* tied into a tie-stall but that she is moving around freely and even encouraged to run around for a good 10-15 minutes. Do not resume feeding of grain too quickly as the grain may have led to the condition in the first place by being fermented in the abomasum and causing the gas initially. How did the grain get to the abomasum when it was intended for the rumen? Not enough effective dry fiber in the ration — not enough hay! You can never feed enough hay to a cow. The more hay or long-leafed baleage in the diet (not haylage), the healthier the gut. It is that simple.

Considerations: There are generally two ways to get a twisted stomach: obstetric based and nutrition based. The "obstetric" LDAs are "acceptable" since the animal had a difficult calving and never got off to a good start, usually contending with a retained placenta and infection and, if they are a first calf heifer, also having to adapt to a very different feeding schedule for the milking string.

However, a "nutritional" LDA is *not* acceptable. This kind of LDA occurs when the cow had a non-eventful calving and got off to a fine start in the first week. Then with the farmer shoveling more and more starch to her (but not enough effective fiber) in order to increase milk, the digestive system goes out of balance and the fourth stomach balloons and floats out of place.

Cows with a left-sided twisted stomach within the first month of lactation will tend to have it recur if only rolled. This is because the rumen has not increased in size enough to keep the abomasum from floating up. The rumen is relatively smaller at this point than later in lactation. Later lactation cows that have a left-sided twist and are

rolled tend to do much better and stay corrected.

Herds that are on a very high forage diet with little grain will have much better results with rolling a cow to correct a twisted stomach than herds that feed a lot of ensiled feeds and grain (like conventional herds do).

If the ping on the left is still audible *after* the rolling of the cow, there is a serious problem. Rolling a cow with a left-sided twist is a primarily therapeutic procedure but becomes diagnostic if an abomasum is stuck in place (due to scarring after an ulcer) or some other odd condition.

Note: *Never* roll a cow that has a suspected or confirmed *right-sided* twisted stomach.

Considerations When Deciding on Surgical or Medical Treatment of a Left-Displaced Abomasum (LDA)

Time since fresh — The longer the time past 2 weeks fresh, the more success with rolling a cow. This is because the rumen will be more at maximal fill in general (than when just fresh), thereby not allowing the abomasum to float up out of place as easily. Unfortunately, most LDAs occur before two weeks fresh.

Ration composition — The longer the fiber length and more quantity of fiber (especially dry hay), the more success with rolling a cow. Cows continuing to eat rations with relatively more corn silage, haylage and especially high moisture shell corn (with little to no dry hay) after being rolled will not respond and will need surgical correction. In barns feeding such rations, just go to the surgical step right away.

Calcium electrolyte status — The more obviously a cow responds to calcium, the more likely the success of also rolling the cow. This is because calcium and other electrolytes will help the strength muscles involved with moving feed through the gut.

Lactation number — Any major change in ration will more strongly affect a first calf heifer, thus needing surgery to correct the condition.

Retained placenta — A first calf heifer with a retained placenta and experiencing a major feed ration change should have surgery done as there are too many negative factors for her to respond well to the medical therapy and rolling. An older cow with a retained placenta that starts eating well after being given calcium electrolytes, allowed to exercise freely and fed long fibrous feeds has a good chance to recover well (unless readily fermented grain feeds are presented too soon).

PROBLEM: EATING & FEED

Eats Hay & Forages But Not Grain

Signalment: First calf heifer fresh about 10 days.

History/Onset: Heifer had an uneventful calving and passed the placenta soon after calving, has been increasing in milk production nicely but over last couple days has not been finishing her grain.

Environment: Tie-stall with component feeding (but could be any system).

Observable Signs: The manure is firmer than the other animals (almost horse-like), and there is not good rumen fill. Depending on the person, an odor like glue or acetone is noticeable from the breath and in the milk bucket.

Physical Exam Findings: Rumen contractions are slow but strong (due to the fiber intake), heart and lungs are normal, udder is normal, the uterus is normal, and the manure is normal except for its firmness. There is good color to the mouth, ears are warm and eyes are pearly white. A urine strip turns purple quickly.

Barn Diagnosis: Ketosis (low blood sugar).

Initial Treatment: IV dextrose (with B vitamins is good).

Follow-up: The IV dextrose is needed to quickly raise the very low blood sugar but the cow needs "fuel in the firebox" (energy in the rumen) and so needs an energy creating addition to the rumen. The industry standard is propylene glycol, a petrochemical derivative and something cows do not like to be dosed with. Glycerin is nearly the same in its action in the rumen but cows really like it. Give 8 oz. orally twice daily as needed. Herbal tinctures with Ceanothus (red root), Chelidonium (celandine), Silybum (milk thistle) and Hydrastis (goldenseal) are particularly useful. Give 20cc orally twice daily. Use of Pyck-Me-Up (Organic) would be beneficial.

Considerations: Primary ketosis can be due to "not enough groceries" — the animal is milking more than what she is being replenished with or due to fat accumulation in the liver. Primary ketosis can cause a twisted stomach (displaced abomasum) just as a twisted stomach can cause ketosis (secondary to the twist). Untreated ketosis can lead to nervous ketosis if proper treatment is not taken in a timely manner.

To prevent ketosis, adequate intake of feed is essential to deliver proper energy levels. Since the liver is involved with the production of ketones, any liver support would be beneficial. The product Reassure delivers rumen-protected choline to the animal's system to be absorbed by the gut and sent to the liver. Vitamin B complex is also helpful and milk thistle (*Silybum marianum*) could be a help, along with celandine, red root and dandelion.

To prevent fatty liver, do not overfeed in the dry period. Excess corn silage can lead to over-condition as well as an enlarged calf, making calving harder (and thus not getting a strong start). Always try to get (or keep) body condition on an animal *prior to* becoming pregnant as it seems that if they gain extra weight after conception fat tends to accumulate around organs (like the liver).

Chewing at the Pipes, Nibbling Herself & Acting Kind of Crazy; Fresh Cow Wants to Eat but Doesn't

Signalment: Third lactation, Holstein, fresh 15 days.

History/Onset: The cow started well but hasn't eaten all her feed in general. She does eat, just not everything like other cows would do.

Environment: Anywhere, anytime.

Observable Signs: The cow is leaning and pushing into the stall rail and is making mouth movements mindlessly. She looks like she is either nibbling or sucking on the pipes around her and occasionally will nibble her own flank. It looks like she wants to eat as she puts her muzzle into the feed but she doesn't actually eat. She has had firm, horse-like manure for the past few days and has backed-off on milk production. The farmer gave her some glycerin one time a few days for what he thought might be ketosis.

Physical Exam Findings: It is difficult to do a physical exam, as the animal wants to constantly move around. However, heart and lungs seem OK, the rumen is moving but slowly, there is no ping (no twisted stomach), the udder is soft (no hard quarter mastitis), there is a normal temperature, the manure in the rectum is indeed very firm like horse manure. The cow has a little bit of urine when "tickled" (stimulated to urinate) and the ketone pad immediately turns dark purple.

Barn Diagnosis: Nervous ketosis.

Initial Treatment: IV dextrose is required as her blood sugar is extremely low (and has been for too long). Even though it is very severe ketosis, only one bottle is needed. The "crazy" symptoms will slowly subside over the course of the next 8-12 hours (unlike rapid improvement of milk fever cows given calcium IV).

Follow-up: Another bottle of dextrose can be given in 6-12 hours as a bottle of dextrose given IV only lasts for about 6 hours in the blood stream. While IV dextrose is definitely needed due to dangerously low blood sugar levels, there also needs to be other blood sugar building compounds given so the cow starts making her own blood sugar again. For organic purposes, glycerin is ideal as it is a three-carbon compound that the rumen bugs can create sugars from (and cows like glycerin). Give 8 oz. twice daily as needed. An alternative would be molasses. Molasses is perhaps best used by pouring onto the cow's grain to get her to eat that (cow's usually don't eat grain when ketotic even though energy is exactly what they need). Giving B vitamins would also be good. Pyck-Me-Up (Organic) is definitely indicated for use.

Considerations: Cows with nervous ketosis don't usually get a twisted stomach. However, if they do have a twisted stomach as well as nervous ketosis, this is a *bad* combination. The nervous ketosis must be addressed first for a day or two. Rolling a cow may be a good way to at least temporarily correcting the twisted stomach until the ketosis is corrected or diminished enough to do surgery. To roll a cow, see the *Eats Very Little and Won't Touch Her Grain* case with accompanying photo.

Not Eating a Thing, Has Been Slowing Down Over The Last Few Days

Signalment: Any animal, any age, male or female.

History/Onset: The farmer is in the middle of harvest season and hasn't been paying as close attention to the animals as usual. This cow has been milking for many months.

Environment: There was a recent feed change, from one ensiled feed to another.

Observable Signs: It is somewhat difficult to get the cow to stand for examination. Cow's belly looks "full" on both sides when standing behind her.

Physical Exam Findings: Heart rate is very increased, there are "smooth" rumen contraction sounds (like the waves hitting the beach — not the standard thunderstorm of a normal rumen), there is a ping over a large area of the right rib cage almost extending to the right elbow, when rapidly pushing the lower right abdomen in and out there is a splashy sound, on rectal palpation a balloon-like structure can be detected at the fingertips on the right side and there is no manure (maybe a couple specks) on the sleeve when finished. The eyes are bit sunken and the eyebrows stay tented when pinched. The ears are cold.

Barn Diagnosis: Right-sided twisted stomach or complete torsion of the stomach (abomasum) depends on severity of symptoms.

Initial Treatment: If the animal stands long enough for physical exam, then do surgery immediately. If the animal was hard to get up to examine and then lays right back down when the examination is finished, it is too late for surgery. Never delay in getting surgery done for this situation. Rolling a cow does *not* work for right-sided twisted stomach situations.

Follow-up: Routine good care for post surgical patient.

Considerations: It is not a surprise when a cow that is fresh about a month and had a history of starting slow over the past few weeks becomes a right-sided twisted stomach at about three or four weeks fresh. Also, most twisted stomachs (displaced abomasums) late in lactation tend to be right sided, partly due to the rumen on the left side being good and full at maximum capacity (unlike early in lactation) and that unsound or moldy ensiled feeds affecting the gut are the primary cause of the digestive upset.

Note: In a normal cow, a ping can normally be heard in the upper area below the short ribs on the right side of the abdomen. This ping represents normal movement of gas through the cow's spiral colon and is not associated with a right-sided twisted stomach. Of course a normal cow will be eating fine whereas a cow with a right-sided twisted stomach won't be.

PROBLEM: EATING & FEED

Doesn't Dig Into Her Feed As She Should — Fresh Three Weeks

Signalment: Thirteen-year-old Holstein, fresh about three weeks.

History/Onset: She hasn't really gotten "started" yet since freshening.

Environment: Anytime, any setting.

Observable Signs: She is bright and alert and eating some; her back is humped up and her head is generally down.

Physical Exam Findings: Low-grade fever — 103 F (39.4 C), slow rumen, pong on right, no pings, uterus OK, enlarged kidney, heart and lungs OK, right hind quarter has dilute looking milk, very positive on the CMT with some swelling of the quarter but it is not hard.

Barn Diagnosis: It may *not* always be one thing wrong! Reasonable conditions include kidney infection, hardware and pending coliform mastitis.

Initial Treatment: IV 250cc Plasma Gold or Bovi-Sera (hyperimmune plasma)), 5cc Immunoboost, 90cc antibacterial tincture (Phyto-Biotic) in 500cc bottle of dextrose, 500cc vitamin C.

Follow-up: Magnet, Phyto-Mast botanical tubes into the RH quarter for four to six milkings in a row, hyperimmune plasma (Plasma Gold or Bovi-Sera) again the next day, given under the skin. Generator Elite (Organic) 0.5 oz. daily, given orally.

Considerations: While it is very likely that the primary problem was the kidney infection (enlarged kidney with low-grade fever and has the stance of an animal with a kidney infection), the right hind quarter may have had a simmering, low-grade infection, which is now becoming worse since the immune system is being taxed with the kidney infection.

Slowing, Eating Less & Less; Generally Sluggish, Passes Very Dark Manure

Signalment: Second calf Holstein, fresh 30 days.

History/Onset: Farmer noticed the cow being different than usual about three days ago.

Environment: Tie-stall, late winter.

Observable Signs: Picking at her feed, seems generally sluggish, slow to get up. Odd "tar-like" diarrhea.

Physical Exam Findings: Increased heart rate and weak pulse, ears are cold, diarrhea is dark and tar-like (obvious from OB sleeve after reaching in rectally). Eye sockets, oral gums and vulva are very pale, almost whitish. Cow lies down rather soon after examination and was hard to rise prior to examination.

Barn Diagnosis: Internal bleeding. Actual cause may never be known, but could be due to an abomasal ulcer (if feeding a hot ration with lots of corn and barley), intestinal bleeding, hardware or cancer.

Initial Treatment: Bleeding ulcers are difficult to treat once they are clinical. However, if the animal will eat, feed *only* grassy hay. Place baking soda on curb to allow her to lick it if she wants. Vitamin K will help

clotting, give one large dose of 100cc under the skin one time. Also, a bottle of calcium and vitamin C (both given IV) can help clotting. Give magnesium oxide pills as an antacid. Give bismuth subsalicylate to patch over any ulcerated areas internally (questionable if allowed for organics — could be technically OK by using human Pepto-Bismol. Clays would be helpful, such as Vit-Ra-Tox. An injection of iron in the muscle could be helpful. Homeopathic Phosphorus for bleeding would be indicated or low potency Ferrum Phos for a bunch of days to build up blood with iron.

Follow-up: Feed dry grassy hay for a few days and monitor closely. Generator Elite (Organic) at high level: 2-4 oz./feeding.

Considerations: The increased heart rate and pale mucous membranes would indicate significant to severe anemia. While a blood transfusion may be considered, transfusions only work when there is an obvious reason for outright blood loss (like a cut milk vein that gets stitched). Internal bleeding is always worse since its location and extent cannot be exactly known.

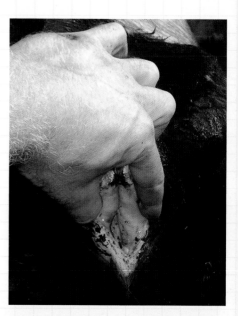

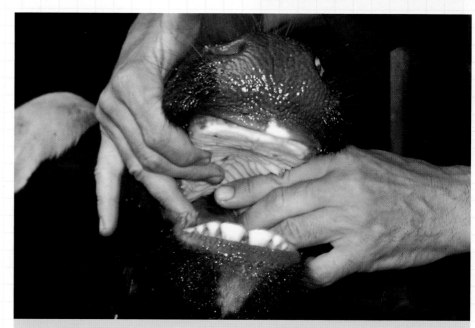

Cow with internal bleeding — notice very pale membrane. This could be either from internal hemorrhage, internal parasitism, or cut of a major vessel along skin or udder. The black dried areas at the edges of the vulva (above) are from the black tar-like diarrhea.

PROBLEM: EATING & FEED

Suddenly Off-Feed From One Milking To The Next

Signalment: Any animal, but mainly larger, mature ones.

History/Onset: The animal was fine in the first half of the day and now only picks at her feed slightly.

Environment: Any barn, barnyard and/or pasture.

Observable signs: Animal is humped up and walks slowly and carefully, not placing much weight on any limb as it touches the ground. The manure, which is not much, is firm looking, almost horse-like.

Physical Exam Findings: Temperature of 103.2 F (39.6 C), increased heart rate, very slow to no rumen activity at all, udder slack (not filled up), on rectal exam the manure is dry and firm. When pinching up the skin above the shoulder blades, the animal stays humped up (cows usually "drop" a bit when pulling up on the skin at the withers).

Barn Diagnosis: Hardware disease.

Initial Treatment: Magnet; IV dextrose with 90cc Phyto-Biotic (strong garlic, ginseng, goldenseal tincture), 250cc Plasma Gold or Bovi-Sera (hyperimmune plasma), 250-500cc vitamin C.

Follow-up: 20cc Phyto-biotic or other strong garlic tincture orally twice daily for four to five days. Build up the bedding so that the animal's front half is visibly higher than her hind end. Pyck-Me-Up (Organic) could be of help.

Considerations: Farms that have been doing any kind of construction work or re-designing existing facilities are at higher risk. Keep cows away from burn piles — they are curious and may lick the ashes and take in metal. If a cow accidentally eats a piece of metal, there is no telling which direction it may poke out of the first stomach where it is lodged. It often goes towards the heart, but could pierce through towards the liver or lungs. A magnet given and in the first stomach (reticulum) pulls the metal upon itself, away from jutting out into other organs. By the way, two magnets are not better than one. You can prove this by placing one magnet on a pipe and pulling it off. Then do the same with two magnets together. There is more "pull" with just one magnet. However, if you can't remember if the cow ever got a magnet, give her one!

Very tucked up; very painful abdomen. This may or may not be due to hardware.

Kneeling continually, will not stand, very anxious stare; obvious pain. This is not a hardware stance but should alert the farmer to seek veterinary attention.

Single Cow is Bloated

Signalment: Fifth lactation Holstein, fresh about four months.

History/Onset: The owner has noted that the cow has bloated in a mild way twice recently during the last month. The cow had been milking really well.

Environment: Wintertime, indoor feeding of stored feeds.

Observable Signs: Obvious bloated rumen.

Physical Exam Findings: Cow's ears are cool to the touch, heart rate is regular if not a bit on the slow side, lungs sound normal and clear, there in no rumen activity and a large pong can be heard when tapping the area, there is some manure from the rectum on the sleeve and the rumen is occupying a very large area internally.

Barn Diagnosis: Free-gas bloat.

Initial Treatment: Pass a 6-8' tube to relieve the gas. The tube needs to be passed within a short but strong metal cylinder to protect it from the cow's teeth. Once the tube is passed, it may need to be slightly pushed and pulled to locate the large area of gas. It will be obvious when the gas area has been found. It can be helpful to have someone pushing at the bloated area once the gas cap has been located. This will help get rid of the most gas possible. Rapid de-bloat is very satisfying.

To pass the tube into the rumen correctly, guide it slightly left of center to get it into the throat and not into the windpipe. (As you and the cow face forward, your left side is also her left side.)

Follow-up: Oftentimes it is good to pump in a gallon of mineral oil to lubricate the gut. Almost as important is to give a bottle of calcium IV (especially to a third lactation cow or older that has been milking well). This will strengthen the muscles of the rumen and the gut to move things through. The product Phyto-Gest (herbal bitters and tonic) would be well worth considering as it has carminatives (to move gas), bitters (increase digestion), and a nerve stimulant (Nux Vomica). Dose is 20cc. Generator Elite (Organic) and Pyck-Me-Up (Organic) will help also.

Considerations: *Any* animal that has sluggish digestion with mild bloat and constipation could benefit from the Phyto-Gest. It is essentially an old time horse colic remedy.

PROBLEM: BLOATING ISSUES

Many Cows are Bloated

Signalment: Cows of various ages and stages of lactation.

History/Onset: The herd has been on the same pasture area for the last four days. The farmer noted than some cows looked very full at the last milking. When bringing in the cows, the farmer saw one dead and a few others severely bloated.

Environment: It is prime pasture season and the cows have been in a lush stand of a clover and ryegrass mix.

Observable Signs: Cows are very puffed up, especially the left side. There is not a triangle seen anymore — it is puffed out now. A few cows are kicking at their sides. None of the bloated animals walk too well.

Physical Exam Findings: No time to do — treat obvious bloat.

Barn Diagnosis: Pasture bloat/ frothy bloat.

Initial Treatment: Get anti-bloat medication into the cows as fast as possible. Cows still standing have the best chance of survival. Give 1 pint of vegetable oil, move the cow around, and repeat the pint of vegetable oil in 15 minutes. Poloxalene (TheraBloat) is allowed for organic emergency treatment (but not embedded within a salt lick). Other kinds of synthetic bloat treatments are not allowed. The vegetable oil actually works very well, if not too late. Some people advocate using Cascara sagrada, a well-known herbal laxative. Cows that are down probably need to be stabbed with a sturdy, sharp knife on the left side behind the last large rib (basically where it is puffed out the worst). Plunge a knife into and through the hide, then turn the knife to allow rapid exit of bloat (air and contents). It seems that during the pasture season, the fresh contents that escape the rumen during an emergency stab don't seem to contaminate the wound site.

Follow-up: Get the cows off the offending paddock! Put them onto a non-legume based pasture for a few days. Generator Elite (Organic) capsules can help re-set them in a positive way.

Considerations: Bloat tends to occur at either end of the grazing season during the cooler days, especially if there has been a frost. Always keep cows off a legume paddock that has frosted for at least two hours after the frost has melted. However, pasture bloat can definitely happen during high summer if the animals have been eating pure stands of legumes for many days in a row. Pasture bloat is made up of millions of tiny bubbles in the rumen. Passing a tube down the cow's throat will not relieve pasture bloat, whereas a tube will relieve the other kind of bloat. The other type of bloat — free-gas bloat, usually only affects one cow in a herd and is usually due to the secondary effects of hardware disease ruining the nerve that runs the process which allows the cow to burp and contracts the rumen regularly. Pasture bloat almost always affects a portion of the herd.

To prevent pasture bloat, *always* feed *dry hay* half an hour prior to putting the cows onto heavy legume pasture. This helps by creating a healthy fiber mat in the rumen as well as filling the cows slightly so they don't "pig out" on the lush pasture too much.

PROBLEM: DIARRHEA ISSUES

Some Lactating Cows Have Diarrhea, Have Become Weak & Are Now Down

Signalment: Any breed, any age; generally lactating cows.

History/Onset: Over the last week or two, about five or six cows of about 100 have broken with diarrhea. At first they kept eating but slowly they gave less milk and now individual ones have become too weak to get up anymore.

Environment: It is early in the spring pasture season. This is a seasonal calving herd (for the most part). The animals affected calved within the last month. The pasture is lush and growing well for this early in the season. The herd is being fed baleage in round bale feeders in the barnyard after they are finished milking and prior to going out to pasture. The cows are fed about 6 pounds of grain in the parlor twice a day at milking times.

Observable Signs: The diarrhea is watery. The cows look a little bit sunken eyed due to dehydration. Other cows also have similar diarrhea but are otherwise normal. The cows that are down are definitely skinny. All cows in the herd are too lean in general.

Physical Exam Findings: Cows have normal to sub-normal temps (are cold), normal udder on California mastitis test (CMT), normal heart and lungs. The rumen is shut down (no contractions). There are no pings (twisted stomachs). There are some pongs on the right side of the abdomen due to the gas in the gut.

Barn Diagnosis: Rumen acidosis.

Initial Treatment: If eating, feed *only* dry grassy hay. Pump the stomach with alfalfa meal and electrolytes and probiotics for nutrition and to re-start the rumen. Add sodium bicarbonate (baking soda) at the rate of 1/2 pound per stomach pumping. Give activated charcoal to bind toxins associated with the rumen acidosis. Add Generator Elite (Organic) to the mix.

Follow-up: Generator Elite (Organic), 2-4 oz./feeding. Take blood tests of the affected cows. Check for total protein: if the protein is less than 5.5, the down cows will probably expire (die), if the protein is 5.5-6.0 they may recover, if the protein is greater than six the prognosis is better.

Considerations: Rumen acidosis is not *only* a condition of confined animals being pushed for maximal production with high levels of starch being fed. Whenever there is not enough effective fiber (dry, grassy hay), rumen acidosis is a possibility. The herd here is being fed lush pasture, baleage and grain (two shots a day). The history and environment listed above is almost enough to figure out the barn diagnosis. Fortunately animals in a pasture situation are more likely to experience less of the secondary consequences that affect the hooves of animals with rumen acidosis since they can walk on the ground instead of being always on concrete. Another possibility in this case would be that the baleage may be unsound and have molds.

Cows Have Diarrhea But Are Eating OK

Signalment: Mainly first calf heifers and a couple second-calf cows. About 10 of 50 are involved.

History/Onset: At first, a single first calf heifer broke with scours and over the course of the last week the rest of the first calf heifers have developed the same signs.

Environment: It is late autumn and the cows have been brought back inside from the remains of the pasture season. It is a tie-stall set up. The herd is being fed dry hay, corn silage, high moisture corn, raw soybeans, and minerals.

Observable Signs: Animals are eating their feed for the most part. The animals with the most bouts of diarrhea are a bit slower but still generally eating. There is no teeth grinding and cows do chew their cud, but a bit less than the normal animals.

Physical Exam Findings: There are increased rumen contractions and they sound "smooth" compared to the normal "thunderstorm" sound. There are some pongs at the hind upper right side of the abdomen. Temperature (take it in the vulva due to the diarrhea and possible false low temperatures in the rectum) is normal. Heart and lungs are normal. No mastitis on CMT plate. Animal is in generally good hydration and is bright and alert.

Barn Diagnosis: Winter dysentery.

Initial Treatment: Since the animals are still eating, feed *only* dry hay until the symptoms disappear and then for a day extra. Then slowly start to feed other feeds back in. Do not feed any silage, baleage, haylage or high moisture corn of any kind (in other words feed no ensiled feeds at all).

Follow-up: Probiotics to re-inoculate the gut. Use Pecti-Cap (Organic) and RumenAider.

Considerations: Winter dysentery is thought to be caused by a rota or corona virus with first calf heifers being the most susceptible. Older animals usually have antibodies against the virus and/or have already experienced it earlier in life. If the diarrhea does not clear up by feeding only dry hay for a few days, or if the symptoms worsen (animals go off-feed, older animals become involved), consider salmonella, BVD or molds in the feed. Seek veterinary attention without delay.

PROBLEM: DIARRHEA ISSUES

Slow to Eat, In Milk a Long Time, Diarrhea Present

Signalment: Third lactation Holstein, fresh six months.

History/Onset: Has had very watery diarrhea recently.

Environment: There was a feed change recently and some of the new silage is a bit moldy.

Observable Signs: Cow has diarrhea and is not eating hardly anything.

Physical Exam Findings: Temperature is 101.2 F (38.4 C), taken in vulva whenever there is diarrhea. The rumen is slow and sounds like a "toilet flushing" rather than the "thunder storm approaching and arriving" heard in a normal cow. Ears are cold, slight dehydration (eyebrow pinch), udder OK, heart and lungs OK. Cow is pregnant three months. There is more diarrhea to come as heard by stethoscope when balloting (pushing in and out) in the lower right abdomen.

Barn Diagnosis: Upset gut (acute enteritis) due to bad feed.

Initial Treatment: Place some dry grassy hay in front of the animal — if she eats it, this is the treatment. Feed only dry grassy or grassy-mixed hay for next few days until manure becomes normal. Feed *no* ensiled feeds of any type — no corn silage, no haylage, no baleage. The cow must have dry hay. Also, take the cow off pasture if it is pasture season. An animal with diarrhea is the only time I ever recommend withholding an animal from pasture during the grazing season. She needs to slow her gut down and dry hay is the absolute best way. *If* she doesn't eat the hay you feed her, she probably should be tubed with antitoxin-type products, with activated charcoal being the primary product. Pecti-Cap (Organic) could also be used. Mineral oil should be considered since this helps line the gut so it doesn't reabsorb any of the toxins. A major property of mineral oil is that none of it is absorbed into the animal's system and completely passes through the digestive tract and on out.

Follow-up: Probiotics of your choice will be good in order to re-inoculate the rumen and gut with beneficial bacteria. However, always remember that probiotics are only half the equation as far as rumen bugs are concerned since protozoa are just as important and cannot be provided unless you take the cud of rumen contents from a donor and directly inoculate a recipient animal within about 5-10 minutes.

Considerations: In addition to the above (but not alone) consider using homeopathic Arsenicum 30C four times daily since its indications are very much described in this case's physical exam findings.

Chronic Diarrhea But Eats Well

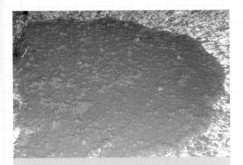

Effortless pipestream diarrhea from a Johne's cow, before bubbles have popped. Typical for Johne's; however, a Johne's positive cow can have relatively normal looking manure too. Be careful!

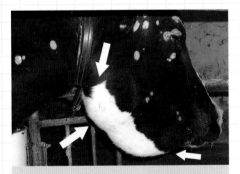

Johne's cow with "bottle jaw" (and ringworm). Bottle jaw swellings usually come on gradually in Johne's cows and is fairly soft to the touch.

Signalment: Third calf Holstein, fresh five months ago.

History/Onset: The cow had a good milk peak (about 100 lbs./day), but then went off-feed one day and has had diarrhea since. Many different probiotics have been used but none have reversed the diarrhea.

Environment: Free stall, tie-stall or bedded pack; any time of year.

Observable Signs: Cow is lean from a good peak milk stage but has not put back on any weight since decreasing in milk. She has a thick pea soup-type diarrhea that is effortless to produce and she produces lots of it. She eats well.

Physical Exam Findings: Rumen is moving well, there is somewhat excessive movement in the small intestine, but no loud gassy sounds, heart and lungs are normal, as are the uterus, kidneys, udder, hair coat, eyes, nose, mouth and behavior.

Barn Diagnosis: Johne's disease, subacute rumen acidosis (SARA).

Initial Treatment: Feed only dry hay for five to seven days to see if the effective fiber provided will slow down the gut and normalize the manure. It may, and if so, go very slowly back to other feeds (ensiled and grain). You can never feed enough dry hay to dairy cows — it is the healthiest feed for their gut outside the pasture season. They may not milk maximally, but their gut will be healthy. Also use Generator Elite (Organic) to enhance a healthy gut.

Follow-up: Test animal for Johne's disease. There are many ways, some cheap and easy (but not quite as accurate) and others more expensive (but very accurate). The milk ELISA test is equal in accuracy to the blood ELISA test. Any ELISA test will only detect antibodies to the actual organism that causes Johne's disease (*Mycobacterium avium* ssp. *paratuberculosis* "MAP"). The manure/fecal test will reveal if the bacteria are actually present, but this takes three to four months to incubate in the laboratory. The PCR test checks the manure for the bacteria's DNA and it takes only a few days for test results. The DNA test is extremely accurate, of course.

Considerations: A few decades ago the colored breeds (Jersey and Guernsey, etc.) had a statistically higher chance of being Johne's positive. This was prior to all the big expansions that have occurred in the dairy sector with the buying in of many cows at a time. Thus at this time, it is more likely that Holsteins will be found to be Johne's positive — simply due to the sheer numbers of Holsteins everywhere these days.

On another point, high producing cows harboring the Johne's bugs but not showing clinical symptoms may be pushed over the line into clinical Johne's if fed a gut irritating diet (high grain relative to forage ratio).

Additionally, this same line of thought should be applied to feeding calves: *never, ever withhold dry hay from calves*, especially milk-fed calves. Irritating the gut with too much grain early in life may pre-

continued on next page

Chronic Diarrhea But Eats Well (cont.)

dispose young animals to developing Johne's later in life if they have been exposed to the Johne's germs early in life. Feeding a high forage diet to calves (with some grain) and strict manure management to keep away adult manure which shed the Johne's germs is critical for at least the first six months of a calf's life (the most susceptible period in life to picking up the Johne's bugs). One final consideration is that while I am a very strong advocate for calves on nurse cows, *never* use a Johne's cow as a nurse cow *i.e.* test potential nurse cows for Johne's status prior to being a nurse cow since the Johne's bugs can be shed in milk (as well as any manure that might be on the teats of a cow).

Older Cow is Down After a Few Days of Diarrhea

Signalment: Seventh lactation Jersey.

History/Onset: The cow had been milking really well. There was a recent feed change and this cow broke with a watery diarrhea soon after eating the new ensiled feed.

Environment: Anywhere, anytime.

Observable Signs: The cow is not eating much of the feeds that are in front if her (dry hay covered over by baleage and topped off with pelleted grain).

Physical Exam Findings: There is a slightly irregular heartbeat (due to loss of electrolytes from scouring), ears are cold, rumen has a "smooth" contraction sound (rather than the normal "thunderstorm" sound), udder is OK, and she is pregnant about 60 days.

Barn Diagnosis: Hypocalcemia, secondary to diarrhea and electrolyte loss.

Initial Treatment: IV calcium product, *hold the bottle no higher than the backbone of the cow.* It should take about 20 minutes to give the bottle on average.

Follow-up: Feed only dry hay (no ensiled feeds) for five days. Also give Pecti-Cap (Organic) and Pyck-Me-Up (Organic).

Considerations: While classical milk fever occurs at calving time, low blood calcium issues are always a possibility with higher producing, older cows that go off-feed or break with diarrhea. They are essentially walking a tight wire and are thrown off by whatever upset their system. They need to be boosted (with IV calcium).

Completely Off-Feed, Has Foul Smelling Bloody Diarrhea With Some Strands of Odd Stringy Looking Material

Signalment: Second calf Holstein, fresh six weeks.

History/Onset: Cow has been doing really well, milking extremely well and was eating everything in front of her "almost like a pig."

Environment: Herd is being fed primarily baleage, haylage, mixed grains and mineral supplement. The upright silo holding the haylage is getting near the bottom and it doesn't smell the best.

Observable Signs: As described in the title to this case.

Physical Exam Findings: Temperature is 104.2 F (40.1 C) when taken in vulva to get the real reading. Dehydrated. No rumen activity. No pings on left but a ping on the right underneath the short ribs. Body is cool to the touch, cool ears. Pupils are somewhat dilated. Mucous membranes are pale pink.

Bloody diarrhea, especially with fever, most likely indicates Salmonella (but possibly BVD). In weanings housed in pens, it could be coccidia (if no fever).

Barn Diagnosis: Salmonella.

Initial Treatment: Immediately tube the cow with activated charcoal and mineral oil to protect the gut from further injury. Give the following: 500cc dextrose with 90cc Phyto-Biotic (garlic-based tincture), 250cc Plasma Gold or Bovi-Sera (hyperimmune plasma), 5cc Immunoboost, 500cc vitamin C, 3-4 liters lactated ringers solution and 1 liter hypertonic saline. Flunixin is allowed for organics and helps a lot with combating endotoxins, so consider adding that into the dextrose.

Follow-up: Phyto-Biotic 15cc orally, three times daily for a few days. Repeat the activated charcoal. Feed on grassy hay. Inoculate the gut with probiotics. Use of Generator Elite (Organic), 0.5 oz. daily would be good.

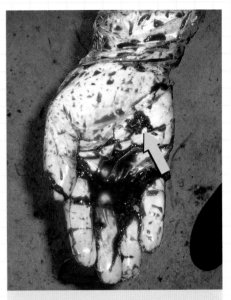

Bloody contents of rectum when removing sleeved hand. Notice the bits of material on the hand — this is sloughed intestinal lining.

Considerations: Give Plasma Gold or Bovi-Sera (hyperimmune plasma) on the following day as well to keep antibodies at a high level initially. Homeopathic Arsenicum 30C or Merc Cor 30C would be indicated.

Note 1: Salmonella is contagious and milk can carry it, without doubt. Bulk tank should not be drunk unpasteurized during a Salmonella outbreak. A few animals can be affected at the same time, but usually it is the ones that are under the most stress — those around calving time and those producing a lot of milk (recently fresh).

Note 2: BVD (Bovine virus diarrhea) can present similarly; however, the initial high fever (105-106 F (40.5-41 C)) usually will have dropped once the diarrhea starts and there may be erosions in the gums and palate of the mouth.

Off-Feed, Mid-Lactation, Recent Feed Change

Signalment: Second lactation Normande-Holstein mix, fresh about five months. May be pregnant two months.

History/Onset: Cow has been off-feed for a few days. This cow has a history of eating up everything greedily.

Environment: There was some wetter than normal ensiled feed being fed out recently.

Observable Signs: Not eating anything and not much, if any, manure being produced. Oddly, wads of cud are seen in both cheeks of the animal. There is a bulge seen on the right abdomen.

Physical Exam Findings: The cow is extremely hyper-excitable and difficult to work with. Temperature is on the low side of normal and she has cold ears. No rumen activity. On rectal palpation, there is a fairly large "balloon" detected to the right of center in the middle of the abdomen. There is no manure on the sleeve.

Barn Diagnosis: An intestinal blockage is very likely — quite possibly a twisted cecum (the balloon which was detected).

Initial Treatment: Surgery would definitely be a good option. If not possible, pump the cow with mineral oil to lubricate the gut. Give IV dextrose with flunixin and a bottle of calcium. Do everything possible to induce diarrhea. Have the animal moving about and *not* tied into a stall. If there is no explosive diarrhea within 6-12 hours, surgery must be done to correct blockage.

Follow-up: Depends if manure starts passing or not. If manure is produced, RumenAider could be used to re-inoculate the gut.

Considerations: The animal in this case photo that shows cud in both cheeks is odd. She was not chewing it. The rumen must have been full and not able to pass digesta down stream and so it came up as "cud."

Note: Cows generally like ensiled feeds. However, ensiled feeds can cause major problems if they are not sound. Most gut problems seem associated with ensiled feed problems. Whenever opening a new silo or bag, *always* feed more dry hay for a few days to buffer the change in ensiled feeds. Cows can take a change in dry hay much, much better than a change in silage.

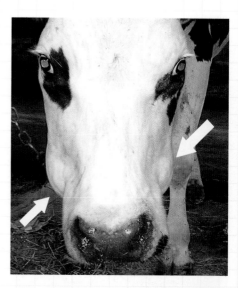

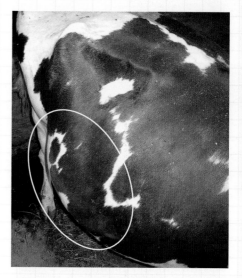

Cow with cud in both sides of mouth that has an abdominal impaction. Circle and arrows show oval-shaped bulge in hind area on right side where there should be none.

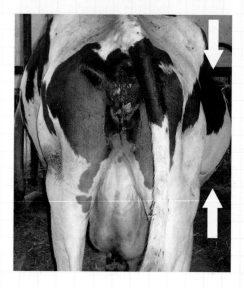

Diarrhea Starting on Cows That Got Into the Grain Room

Signalment: Cows of various ages and various stages of lactation.

History/Onset: When the farmer came back for milking after an all day meeting, he found a few cows in the grain room. Some others were nearby and when chased away, they seemed a bit wobbly.

Environment: The grain room is near the barn yard. Someone left an electric wire down when driving the tractor around the cow yard to clean it. The cows must have been curious and eventually found their way to the grain area. About 20 animals are affected from the herd of 150.

Observable Signs: Cows are somewhat dull. Some have diarrhea developing. All have cold ears.

Physical Exam Findings: The rumens are not functioning, there is elevated heart rate and some increased breathing rate going on. No cud chewing in the 20 animals that ate the grain. On rectal palpation, the contents are becoming very loose and grain is evident when pulling the sleeve out.

Barn Diagnosis: Rumen acidosis.

Initial Treatment: *Time is critical.* Pump each and every cow with activated charcoal, baking soda (¹/₂ pound), and mineral oil. The mineral oil is not absorbed by the animal's system and coats the gut to prevent absorption of the offending grain. Also 8-10 "pink pills" (magnesium oxide) to offset the low pH.

Follow-up: Probiotics and dry hay for however long it takes for the manure to become normal again. Feed no ensiled feeds until normalization of manure. Generator Elite daily, 2-4 oz. per feeding.

Considerations: Like the case where the herd was being fed lush spring pasture, grain and baleage (but not enough *effective dry fiber* in the form of dry, grassy hay), this herd went on to do well with no hoof problems. This is likely due to the animal spending most of the time out on pasture and not confined to concrete.

One Down of Eight Bred Heifers That Got Out & Are Eating Some Hedges

Signalment: Fourteen- to twenty-month-old Jerseys.

History/Onset: Farmer just noticed this when coming out of the barn after morning milking.

Environment: It is wintertime and no other green vegetation is growing, just the evergreen hedges around the house.

Observable Signs: Heifers are actively eating the twigs with small flat green needles. The bush usually has some translucent reddish berries with a hollow tube-center in the autumn.

Physical Exam Findings: No need to examine animals as treatment must be started immediately.

Barn Diagnosis: Yew poisoning.

Initial Treatment: Call vet immediately. Use activated charcoal — a whole 300cc tube immediately given to all animals possibly involved. Do not skimp.

Follow-up: Repeat the activated charcoal in four hours.

Considerations: This is a terrible situation but unfortunately does occur. The animals that get out can't help themselves from going to the only green vegetation available. Yew poisoning can kill animals in as short as 30 minutes. All ruminants (sheep, goats, etc.) are as equally affected.

PROBLEM: CALVING ISSUES

Cleanings Hanging Out; Cow Was Confirmed Pregnant Earlier

Signalment: Second calf Holstein, bred about three or four months.

History/Onset: Farmer noticed that the cow had a lot of discharge from vulva the last two days and her tail was slightly extended. After morning milking it looked like the cow had a bit of cleanings (placenta) hanging out.

Environment: Anytime, anywhere.

Observable Signs: Cow is fine other than the cleanings being seen.

Physical Exam Findings: Heart and lungs are normal, rumen is functioning normally, no pings (no twisted stomach), the udder is slightly enlarged compared to normal, temperature of the cow is normal — 102 F (38.9 C), when reaching in directly (into vulva and vagina), a small calf is detected halfway in the birth canal and still half way in the uterus (womb). It seems that the sack (placenta) is still around the fetus.

Barn Diagnosis: Abortion.

Initial Treatment: Manually remove the fetus and find a very clean place to look at it.

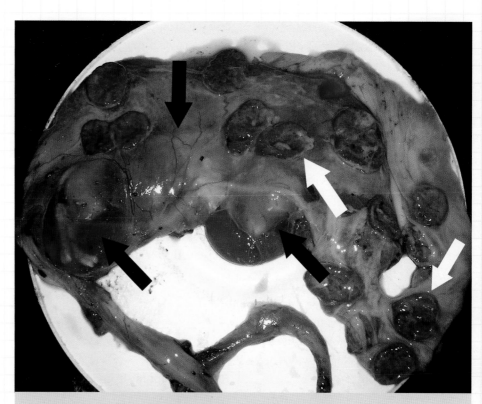

A calf aborted after about three or four months of gestation. The entire calf with its placenta has been expelled. Black arrows point to the hooves, trunk and head. The cotyledons of the calf are very easily seen (white arrows).

Follow-up: The cow will most likely go on normally after this event, but she should be watched a little more closely for a couple days. To double check if a cow is still pregnant later in pregnancy, you can try "bumping the calf." By repeatedly pushing in and out at the lower *right* abdomen, you will feel (bump) the calf as a solid structure if it is there. A calf must be of reasonable size to accomplish this (generally at six-and-a-half or more months of pregnancy). Bumping a calf is good to do when drying off a cow, especially if you have any question about her pregnancy or if she looks over-conditioned.

Considerations: In a 50 cow herd, a single abortion in a year is "accept-able" since spontaneous abortions do occur in all species. However, if other abortions have occurred within a small time frame (*i.e.* within a month or two), diagnostic work-up to figure out the cause of the abortion problem would be wise to do.

If possible, submit the *clean* fetus and placenta to a diagnostic lab. In general, abortions that occur between 30 and 90 days of pregnancy may be associated with BVD (bovine viral diarrhea), whereas abortions that occur between four to six months may be associated with Leptospira (Lepto) bacteria and abortions that occur at seven or eight months of pregnancy may be due to Neospora. Depending on what the lab results show, consider vaccinating if the abortion is due to Lepto.

If the calf is submitted, then the actual cause can be determined whereas if only a blood sample is drawn from a cow with suspected abortion or early embryonic death, then only a titer will be reported. A titer is essentially a reflection of the immune system of the animal, specifically for the germ being looked for. Keep in mind that vaccinations will make the titer more difficult to interpret since vaccines stimulate the immune system. If there is a high titer for BVD and nothing else, then BVD may be a problem, especially if there is a history of irregular heats and possible early embryonic death. There could be a persistently infected (PI) animal in the herd (any age), which is loading the environment with live BVD particles (that vaccination cannot overcome).

Until a BVD PI animal is identified and removed from the herd, no BVD vaccine of any sort will work and there will chronic underlying problems in the whole herd. If a Lepto titer is high, start vaccinating since isolating and identifying the Lepto is very time consuming. If Neospora is found to be the cause, try to ride out the abortion storm as Neospora abortions tend to fade away after a few months.

Twinning can definitely be the cause of abortion — so always check for a twin.

Some animals will show signs of heat right after they abort — do *not* breed — wait at least two or three weeks until next heat to breed.

Softball-Sized Round Mass Coming Out of the Vulva

Signalment: Dry Holstein cow coming into her fourth lactation.

History/Onset: The farmer noticed a bulging from the vulva slowly enlarging over the last few weeks. The cow is due in three weeks.

Environment: Anytime, anywhere.

Observable signs: The "softball" shows when the cow is lying down but goes back in when she stands up.

Physical Exam Findings: The cow is totally fine in all respects, except for the softball size mass. The pregnancy is fine; the cervix is closed and there is only a slight tacky dark golden discharge.

Barn Diagnosis: Prolapsing vulvo-vagina.

Initial Treatment: None needed for dairy breeds. This is a condition due to increasing estrogens associated with late stage pregnancy. There is no real treatment needed, as it is self-limiting (finished at calving).

Follow-up: Monitor. If the mass goes back in whenever the cow gets up, it should be fine. If the mass stays out even when standing, it can become dried up and also have straw or other environmental material stuck to it. Before this starts happening, it should be manually placed back in and sutured by a veterinarian to close down the gaping opening.

Considerations: If this condition persists after a few weeks of calving, it must be sutured in or a raging infection will likely happen. Homeopathic causticum would be indicated for loose ligaments, twice daily for 10 days.

PROBLEM: REPRODUCTIVE ISSUES

Dry Cow, Seems to be Getting Bigger & Bigger

Signalment: Holstein finished her third lactation, pregnant about seven months and dry for the last three weeks.

History/Onset: Seems like over the last few days, maybe a week, the cow shows both sides of her belly becoming very large.

Environment: Cow is in a tie-stall with other cows and observed daily.

Observable Signs: As stated, cow is enlarging much more than other dry cows and a little slower to eat now.

Physical Exam Findings: Increased heart rate, lungs normal, temperature normal, rumen slow but functioning, no pings/no twisted stomach, udder soft, cow is bright and alert, hydration normal. On rectal palpation, a huge volume of fluid is detected and no calf is felt.

Barn Diagnosis: Hydrops allantois or hydrops amnion. It really doesn't matter exactly which as either one is a severe accumulation of fluid in the uterus.

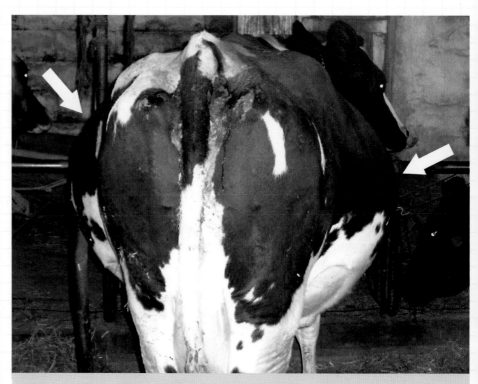

Dry cow, seems to be getting bigger and bigger.

Initial Treatment: Consider salvage for beef immediately since the condition will continue indefinitely until calving. If not wanting to do beef, consider inducing calving with PGF_{2alpha} and dexamethasone (cow will no longer be organic). Be prepared to give lots of IV fluids to replace the massive amount of fluids that will be lost when calf is delivered.

Follow-up: Attentive care after inducing calving.

Considerations: Dry cows looking very full as shown in the photo for this case sometimes have a right-sided torsion of the abomasum (RTA). An RTA is not common, but it is more common than the very rare condition of hydrops. This must be ruled out.

Calved Two Weeks Early

Signalment: Third lactation mixed breed.

History/Onset: Cow was due in two weeks (had only one artificial insemination date and no bull is in the area, including neighboring farm).

Environment: Any season, any type of barn.

Observable Signs: The cow was found with a dead calf when the farmer came out in the morning. The cow has not yet passed the placenta. She is up and eating, looking bright and alert.

Physical Exam Findings: Reaching into the cow, a twin is detected.

Barn Diagnosis: Twins.

Initial Treatment: Extract calf.

Follow-up: A uterine infection is almost guaranteed in these situations. Therefore use antiseptics everyday until the placenta is removable (usually the seventh or eighth day with twins).

Twins. Notice the yellowish color on one twin — this is meconium staining (the first manure a newborn makes) and indicates the calf was stressed in-utero prior to delivery. This calf was stuck and needed re-positioning. Reaching in afterwards revealed a twin. The cow was about one or two weeks early for projected calving date (common for twin situations).

Considerations: Twins are often the cause for early calvings. Depending on how early from actual expected date will often determine if the twins live or not. In 95 to 99 percent of the cases of twins, whether two weeks early or at calving date, there will not be complete release of both placentas by the cow.

Due to Calve, But Is Down & Has Severe Diarrhea After Accidentally Getting Into Grain Bin Yesterday

Signalment: Eight-year-old Jersey cow, pregnant and due to calve within a few days (one AI breeding to sexed semen — heifer calf likely).

History/Onset: Two days ago the cow somehow got into the sweet feed (molasses grain) in the horse side of the stable. Might have eaten half a bag (25 lbs. or more).

Environment: Anywhere, anytime.

Observable Signs: Cow is down and bloated. Diarrhea has many undigested grain particles in it.

Physical Exam Findings: Cold ears, splashy sounds when balloting the gassy rumen, foul manure, fast heart beat; cervix is not yet dilated to calve, normal discharge; udder is normal for pregnancy.

Barn Diagnosis: Grain overload with severe rumen acidosis.

Initial Treatment: Pass a tube into rumen and relieve free gas bloat. Then pump in activated charcoal as an antidote and mineral oil to lubricate/coat the gut so it won't reabsorb toxins. Give IV fluids including dextrose, 3-4 liters lactated ringers solution, 300-400cc sodium bicarbonate, and calcium (she is an older Jersey).

Follow-up: If bloat does not get relieved much, place a rumen trocar into the rumen to relieve distention. Can try to siphon out liquid contents of rumen either during the initial tube passed through the mouth or if using a small tube placed through the rumen canula.

Considerations: Terminal C-section. If no better in six to eight hours, consider a C-section to save the calf prior to the cow expiring. Such a C-section could be done immediately at the initial visit. After C-section, humanely euthanize the cow. This makes the best of a sad situation.

Make sure that there is colostrum available — either milk the mother cow prior to C-section or get some from a neighbor. If none is available at all, use bulk tank milk and add First Defense boluses to give some measure of protection against *E. coli* bacteria and rota-corona

Terminal C-section to save the life of the calf on extremely ill cow (grain overload two days before). Incising the uterus to expose the calf leg.

Removing the calf from the cow.

viruses. Hyperimmune plasma, (Plasma Gold or Bovi-Sera) 100-200cc given under the skin and 1cc Immunoboost would be very appropriate as well. An IV mixture of 700cc lactated ringers solution, 200cc sodium bicarbonate and 100cc dextrose will help reverse any metabolic acidosis that the calf acquired when in-utero. I give IV to calves using a 16 gauge, 1-inch needle. Wetting the calf's jugular vein helps locate it and having a person holding the head steady and firmly so no movement can take place is critical to keeping the needle in the vein.

Stimulating the calf to breathe by rapidly "pecking" the lower area of the center of the nose with an 18 gauge needle.

Author supporting head of calf for a picture.

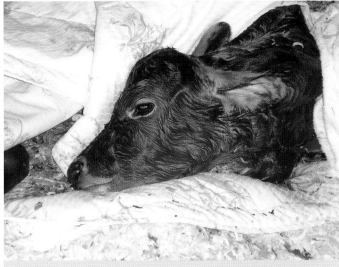

Newborn calf weak but breathing and resting. Sodium bicarbonate IV is very helpful to reverse the metabolic acidosis many calves experience during a hard birth (especially from a known acidosis cow).

Calf at one-day old, sitting up on its own.

Due to Calve Within Two Days and Not Eating

Signalment: Six-year-old Holstein, bred by artificial insemination, settled on first service and coming into her fourth lactation. No bull present on farm (to potentially create a different breeding date).

History/Onset: Was totally normal and eating until about 12 hours ago.

Environment: Cow was separated apart from other dry cows to watch closely and is in her own box stall now. Bedding is sand.

Observable Signs: Not eating, getting up and down occasionally, large amount of mucous hanging down from vulva, perhaps a tinge reddish.

Physical Exam Findings: First thing to do is to wash up the vulva and reach in the cow to feel where in the birth process the cow is. If normal, the cow's cervix will probably be one or two fingers dilated, maybe more. If so, then be happy that the cow is being normal. Cows will generally back off feed about 12 hours prior to calving.

Barn Diagnosis: Impending calving.

Initial Treatment: Allow to progress.

Follow-up: Monitor.

Considerations: Some farmers will not reach into a cow. Why not? Farmers *must* reach into a cow that is near due if there are (*any*) concerns. There is no other option since most problems will revolve around the actual calving process if they are that near to calving. If the cow has cold ears and is older, strongly consider giving calcium IV to immediately boost bloodstream calcium. Check the cow's udder — if one quarter looks much larger or is harder compared to the others, strip it out to check if it is watery. Most secretion at this point should be honey-like. If watery, coliform mastitis is probably starting. See section for *Watery Secretion From Quarter* since coliform mastitis often occurs within a week before or after calving since the teat plugs are dissolving prior to calving and after calving a cow may be laying down too much due to being weak from low calcium (which may give leaky teats and allow for environmental germs to enter the gland).

If the cow's ears are warm and the udder is in fine shape, then giving Caulophyllum (botanical tincture) or a Caulophyllum homeochord (multi-potency) homeopathic remedy would be indicated to simply help uterine contractions.

Try not to move a cow that is in early labor to a new location. This can interrupt them and possibly lead to a stillborn calf.

"COLD + OLD" = CALCIUM!

PROBLEM: CALVING ISSUES

Straining & is Due to Calve

Signalment: Second calf Holstein (coming into third lactation). She is AI bred and due in two days.

History/Onset: About 12 hours ago cow started to strain like she was going to calve.

Environment: Box stall with nice fresh bedding of corn fodder.

Observable Signs: Cow pushes and strains but is not advancing to give birth. Tail is extended. Not eating. Grinds teeth occasionally. Uncomfortable.

Physical Exam Findings: Direct examination of birth canal reveals a twisting, auger-like feel. The calf feels "far in."

Barn Diagnosis: Uterine torsion/twisted uterus.

Initial Treatment: Must correct the uterine torsion. The main idea is to untwist the cervix and uterus. This can be done by having a veterinarian flip the calf over within the uterus (this is an art that veterinarians learn while on the job) or by rolling the cow. If rolling the cow, the cow needs to be dropped and rolled in the same direction that the twist is going (see *Eats Very Little & Won't Touch Her Grain* case). This

Typical posture of a cow that has a uterine torsion (twisted uterus): straining to calve but not advancing. Notice the tail extended out. This is typical of a cow with calving difficulty and especially a twisted uterus.

needs at least three people and a 35-foot (12 meter) rope. Once the cow is pulled down with the rope, she needs to be rolled in the direction that the twist is going. One person is needed to pull the back legs over and one person needs to pull the front legs and the brisket over. The third person sits on the belly in front of the udder of the cow and remains sitting upon the cow as the cow is rolled. This is to keep the calf in place.

When accomplished, stand the cow up and reach in the birth canal again. If untwisted, there will be no auger-like feel anymore. If still twisted, repeat the process until corrected. This may take a few times. Always have a heavy person sitting on the belly of the cow when rolling her.

Follow-up: If the calf is alive, let the cow be on her own as mother nature will likely continue with the calving process now that the cervix can fully

dilate. The cow should be calved in by the end of the day or within six to eight hours from the correction of the twist. If not fresh by then, re-examine. If the calf is dead, you need to extract the calf at time of correction since "the window of opportunity" is passed. The last ring of the cervix is usually a bit smaller after correcting the twist. If it is an older cow, it will flexible from previous calvings. A first calf heifer-to-be won't have such flexibility. In either case, you will need to *carefully* work the cervix up over the crown of the calf's head. If it feels pretty tight when accomplished, allow time for the head and neck of the calf to help expand the area.

It is critical to realize that the cow's productive life should not be put at risk by being impatient to get the calf out. If too forceful when things are tight, rips happen in the vaginal birth canal and serious consequences easily occur. It is better to deliver a fresh dead calf than force it out and likely ruin both cow and calf.

Considerations: An older cow may need calcium IV and dextrose IV to replenish her strength since she was already pushing against a "closed door" prior to correcting the twist. Giving it in the vein is important to deliver rapid strength since the calving process is happening. Blue cohosh (*Caulophyllum thalictroides*) would be excellent to give as well. I would recommend it in the tincture form (as opposed to homeopathic form) since that plant juice is well known to offset uterine weakness.

Not Standing Yet — Fresh a Couple Hours

Signalment: Fifth lactation Jersey, had a live heifer calf on her own two hours ago.

History/Onset: The cow was checked a few hours ago and had just started the calving process. Checked again and she had calved in and was licking the calf. Two buckets of luke warm water were given and she drank both.

Environment: Anytime, anywhere.

Observable signs: The cow will not rise when prompted; she hasn't yet passed the placenta, there is some twitching of her skin (despite lack of flies), and she opens her mouth when you approach her.

Physical Exam Findings: Cold ears, dilated pupils of the eyes, milk is leaking from the teats, the placenta is firmly attached still, her temperature is 99.8 F (37.7 C).

Barn Diagnosis: Milk fever (low calcium).

Initial Treatment: IV calcium bottle (23% calcium, Cal-Phos #2, CMPK, etc). *Hold the bottle no higher than her backbone!* It should take about 10-15 minutes to give, if using a 14 gauge IV needle. Wait one hour before giving another bottle, unless listening to the heart regularly for any indication of irregular beats.

Follow-up: If the cow gets up and starts eating and being otherwise normal, no more treatment is needed. However, a milk fever cow can often need at least a little more calcium enhancement. An oral paste or liquid Pyck-Me-Up (Organic) is OK at this point. Be very, very careful about drenching any cow with anything. Hold the head roughly parallel to the ground (*never* have the nose to the sky, as it is much easier to get things into the lungs that way), and give a little bit, then let her swallow, then some more and let her swallow again. *Never, ever just let a fluid run into a cow's mouth.* Actually, giving a bottle IV is much more effective, you just need to hold the bottle *no higher than the backbone.*

In 15 years, I have never killed a cow when treating for milk fever IV by using the "no higher than backbone" method. Any other kind of bottle you can run in as fast as you want (vitamin C, hypertonic saline, dextrose, lactated ringers) just *not* calcium products.

Also, you could give the 23% calcium under the skin, injecting about 100cc in five individual areas. This will give slow absorption. Do not do this with CMPK or other mixed formulations, as abscesses tend to occur.

Considerations: Milk fever is always an emergency. Why? Just as the muscles of the legs are too weak to rise, all the muscles of the body are very weakened and thus the uterus can fall out (prolapsed uterus), the rumen muscles won't turn over normally and bloat will occur, the muscles of the teat ends won't tighten properly and leaking milk will occur (high potential for coliform mastitis).

Cows that had milk fever previously tend to get it again the next time fresh and on and on. If a cow is treated for milk fever with IV calcium products and does not respond, check her milk and see if coliform mastitis is also happening. Also consider a pinched nerve. The main difference between a pinched nerve cow and a milk fever cow is that a pinched nerve cow will be bright and alert, eating and drinking water but cannot rise while a milk fever cow will usually be tired looking and depressed (but so will a down coliform cow!).

Another consideration in a fresh cow that is down but bright and alert is low phosphorus.

One interesting way to prevent milk fever is to give 2 ounces apple cider vinegar (not white vinegar), twice daily for at least two weeks prior to calving. It seems to have a slightly acidifying effect on the system, which will allow for the continual slow release of just enough calcium from the bones into the blood stream to prevent milk fever.

Large Mess Sticking Out of Her Hind End — Fresh Overnight

Signalment: Fifth lactation Holstein, fresh a few hours.

History/Onset: Last time the cow was checked (late at night) she hadn't yet calved. Now she's calved in, prior to morning milking.

Environment: Anywhere, anytime.

Observable signs: The cow is down and not very alert, the large blob is behind her (often sagging into the gutter).

Physical Exam Findings: No need, just call veterinarian immediately.

Barn Diagnosis: Prolapsed uterus.

Initial Treatment: This is a true emergency, as the cow can die due to vessel rupture internally. This will take a minimum of two people to work on. The cow's legs need to be extended behind her in order to elevate the rump somewhat and so she cannot get up. Someone needs to hold the tail out of the way. If the placenta is still attached, it needs to be very, very carefully peeled away from each caruncle ("button"). Then the veterinarian needs to place the uterus back into the body. This can be an extremely hard undertaking if the uterus has been out long as fluid can accumulate in it. If the

uterus was just pushed out in the last 30-60 minutes, it is sometimes a quick job to place it back into the cow. This is the only time it is good to have a retained placenta as the placenta covers over the uterine walls and keeps dirt away.

Follow-up: In older cows the primary reason for a prolapsed uterus is low blood calcium levels (milk fever). Give IV calcium *after* the uterus has been placed back into the cow. If given beforehand, it can make the cow strong and she will perhaps fight your efforts to restrain her properly as well as making the actual work of replacing the uterus much harder. Occasionally an epidural anesthetic is needed to stop the cow from straining as they all do when the uterus is being passed back through the cervix. After the uterus is placed back in the body, it is good to place a thick suture through the vulva area to keep "the door shut." Also try to keep the hind end slightly higher than the front of the cow.

Considerations: First calf heifers can push their uterus out if they keep straining after the calving. This is why it is important that you *get an animal to stand up shortly after it has calved in* (regardless of age) — the standing position will normally help keep the uterus in the abdomen whereas the uterus has a higher likelihood of flopping out if the animal is lying down. In almost all cases, the uterus will be pushed out within the first couple hours after calving. If the prolapse occurs on the second day fresh, this is very difficult to fix since the cervix is somewhat closed down as compared to right after calving. Sometimes the

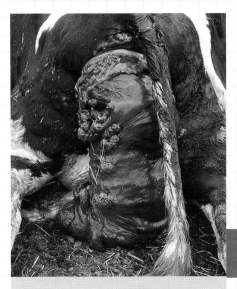

Prolapsed uterus set-up to be replaced. Need two come-alongs, two ankle hobbles and a digging iron for an outdoor prolapse.

placenta is all that is coming forth and may look like a lot more than usual and occasionally trigger a call to the vet for a prolapsed uterus. Be happy if it is just the placenta!

If the animal is truly strong and standing, then the replacement must be done with the cow standing. Some veterinarians prefer this position, but most prefer the cow lying down with the legs pulled out backwards and shackled to something to reduce movement.

PROBLEM: CALVING ISSUES

Cool Ears, "S" Bend in Her Neck — Cow is Fresh & Hasn't Responded to Calcium Gluconate IV

Signalment: Seventh calf Jersey, fresh three days.

History/Onset: Cow needed a bottle of calcium prior to calving due to cold ears and not advancing with calving. She had milk fever the last three times fresh.

Environment: Box stall.

Observable Signs: Cow has cool ears and always seems to have a slightly noticeable "S" bend in her neck. Cow only feebly responds to 23% calcium borogluconate IV. Has gotten up each day for a little while but goes down again and has gotten calcium treatments. These treatments keep her from going completely flat out and bloating but aren't strong enough to get her going for real.

Physical Exam Findings: No watery mastitis detected, cow passed the placenta 24 hours after calving, and her hind legs are positioned normally when she is sitting. However, there is a distinct curve in her neck.

Barn Diagnosis: Low potassium (hypokalemia).

Initial Treatment: IV CMPK or some sort of potassium delivering product. Also give Pyck-Me-Up (Organic) orally, measured out that the cow receives at least 60 grams of potassium in a day.

Follow-up: Can give calcium gluconate under the skin for slow release (don't do with CMPK or you will get an abscess). Must be very clean about this and pour alcohol over the skin area where the needle insertion will be.

Considerations: There may be low phosphorus as well. If the above does not work, consider giving one whole complete Fleet Enema fluid IV (diluted in dextrose or other IV fluids). This will provide phosphate in a form the cow's system will be able to use immediately. If a cow is bright, alert, eating and drinking and cannot get up, it is possibly a pinched nerve (especially if the history includes a hard calving). If a few cases in a row are bright, alert, drinking and down, phosphorus deficiency is most likely.

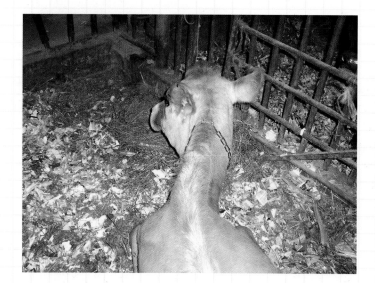

Cows are fresh and haven't responded to 23% calcium gluconate IV. The slight "S" shape in neck can indicate low potassium.

Cannot Get Up & Had a Very Hard Calving

Signalment: First-calf Holstein heifer.

History/Onset: The heifer was struggling to calve in the night before. The farmer assisted the calving by using mechanical force to extract the calf. The calf was born dead.

Environment: A box stall.

Observable Signs: The cow is bright and alert, eating and drinking well, but cannot lift her hind end off the ground more than a few inches.

Physical Exam Findings: There is a minor rip in the birth canal (vagina) at the 10 o'clock position. The placenta is retained. One of the ankles is very "cocked" (bent tightly).

Barn Diagnosis: Pinched nerve.

Initial Treatment: Homeopathic Arnica and Hypericum. Acupuncture (see photos for this case), depending if there is an acupuncture veterinarian in the area. Possibly aspirin, but better yet would be flunixin to keep inflammation and swelling to a minimum (best to use it prior to full blown inflammation). Provide good traction! Farmers give up on these animals way too quickly. If given good husbandry and care, an animal may rise on its own after 10-12 days.

Close up of acupuncture needles and attachments for electrical stimulation.

Cow with pinched nerve receiving electroacupuncture treatment. If the cow eats hay while being treated, they usually rise a few hours later.

In areas dense with dairy farms, there is usually a water tank flotation device available. These are excellent devices as they allow for the animal's circulation to be normal (instead of lying on one side all the time) and allows the animal to stand with the help of the water (floats the cow). Float tanks also can predict the future of the cow. If she walks out and keeps going – great! If she walks out then lies down and can't get up, re-float (also give calcium if older). If she goes down with the water as the float is being drained, she is permanently damaged and salvage for hamburger would be wise.

Follow-up: Try to get the animal up as often as possible in the day to have her use and exercise the limbs. If the cow's hoof "knuckles" over when trying to stand, manually correct it and maybe even put your foot on the front side of the ankle to keep it in the normal position.

Considerations: Most of the time, the bad leg will have its *ankle* bent almost at a right angle. However, occasionally, the affected leg will extend way forward under the animal. This situation is generally worse. If it is an older cow, the pinched nerve may have occurred due to blood calcium at the onset of calving, slowing down the expulsion of the calf through the birth canal and thereby compressing and "pinching" a nerve. Therefore, if common signs of milk fever are present as well (skin twitching at the shoulder blades, cold ears, not eating and drinking well) treat with IV calcium products.

Retained Placenta After Calving

Signalment: Second lactation Holstein, fresh four days.

History/Onset: Had a difficult calving due to a large bull calf and required assistance.

Environment: Box stall with chopped paper as bedding. Weather is cold and damp.

Observable Signs: Cow is a bit sluggish eating and the placenta is visible. Some foul odor is noticeable.

Physical Exam Findings: Normal temperature, heart and lungs are OK, rumen is slow but functioning, no twisted abomasum, manure is normal, CMT positive slightly on RH. Uterus has some foul watery fluid that is expelled when cow stains as she is being checked directly through the birth canal, cervix and into the uterus.

Barn Diagnosis: Retained placenta (RP) and uterine infection (metritis).

Initial Treatment: The goal is to introduce antiseptics into the uterine environment before the cervix closes and traps bad things in there. It matters little what you put into the uterus, just make sure it gets done — *and not only one time*. It needs to be done repeatedly, day after day, until the placenta is fully removed.

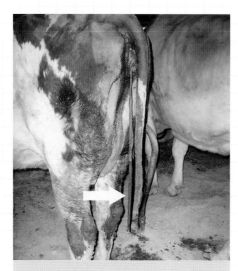

Retained placenta.

Retained placenta.

There are many good products on the market and capsules are probably the easiest to work with when the cow is fresh. I use iodine pills, administering the equivalent of 1 gram daily. Some people rail against iodine in the uterus. This is unfounded. Another excellent product is the Van Beek Royal Uterine capsules, which is an essential oil mixed in with a powder in a capsule. Herbal Caulophyllum orally 10cc three times daily for three to four days. Homeopathic Pyrogenium three times daily.

Follow-up: Every day after the 5th day fresh, the placenta should be checked to see if it will gently tease out. Do not try to remove a retained placenta before it is ready or it will tear off, making it very hard to deal with what remains in the uterus.

Note: The harder the calving, the earlier the cow freshened (than when she should have), or if there were twins born will mean that it takes longer for the placenta to pass. Almost always by the eighth or ninth day the cleanings, rotten and stinking, will be able to be freely removed with gentle tugging.

Considerations: If there is a pattern of cows calving on their own on time and not cleaning, definitely think about using an injection of selenium and vitamin E (MuSe) about two or three weeks prior to anticipated calving date, especially if in an area that is known to be low in soil selenium. If it is only third lactation cows or older that aren't expelling their placenta after an unassisted calving, consider low blood calcium levels as a factor. Talk to your nutritionist on how to correct this to prevent further problems.

Note: Cows normally pass the afterbirth within six to eight hours of calving. In my experience, cows that do drop the entire afterbirth anytime *after* that time period will have a uterine infection. So, if a cow passes the placenta at 24-48 hours after calving, treat as described above under Initial Treatment.

PROBLEM: REPRODUCTIVE ISSUES

The Vet Says the Cow is Cystic

Signalment: Second calf cow, fresh about 100 days.

History/Onset: The cow checked fine at her first reproduction check between three and five weeks fresh.

Environment: Wintertime feeding in a free stall barn.

Observable Signs: No heats shown, nothing else is noticed.

Physical Exam Findings: When reaching in to the cow during a routine reproduction check, the veterinarian felt a cyst on the right ovary, which she couldn't gently rupture.

Barn Diagnosis: Cystic cow.

Initial Treatment: Ask the vet to try to rupture the cyst. It is oftentimes possible if it is a follicular cyst. If it is a luteal cyst, it is more difficult. If the cyst cannot be ruptured or the vet does not want to rupture it for fear of hemorrhage, for a right-sided cyst use homeopathic Apis Mellifica 30C twice daily for five days in a row, then follow-up with Natrum Mur 30c twice daily for three days in a row. If it is a left-sided cyst, use homeopathic Lachesis in place of the Apis and follow with Natrum Mur.

Follow-up: The homeopathic approach usually yields satisfactory results. If not, use the Heat Seek tablets, two tablets twice daily in the mouth for a treatment time of 12 days. If the veterinarian knows how to do acupuncture, injections of 5cc vitamin B_{12} at each of the acupuncture points of bladder meridian 22 through 26 on the side of the cyst can be helpful.

Considerations: Cows can become cystic for many reasons. Included are: (1) when a cow starts putting back on body condition after she has been in peak milk production and skinny, (2) after a summer heat spell and the cooler autumn weather resumes, (3) high producing cows, and (4) family tendency. There are other reasons as well, but since hormone shots won't be used on organic farms, the detailed physiology processes probably don't need to be discussed.

Repeat Breeders: Some animals will not settle (conceive) though they are anatomically normal. They come into heat every 21 +/- days, get bred, and don't conceive. These are usually Holsteins in herds where artificial insemination is used.

Here is what I usually suggest:

1) breed the cow as soon as you see a heat. In other words, don't wait 12 hours. The egg is most receptive when it is freshest. And — would a bull wait 12 hours?

2) use a different breed of bull, like a Jersey, Milking Shorthorn, etc. For whatever reason, this often works.

3) use two tablets of Heat Seek one to two days before anticipated heat and also on the day of breeding.

White Discharge on Tail

Signalment: Second calf cow, fresh three weeks.

History/Onset: Had a hard calving due to having a leg turned back and needed assistance to correct it. Cow didn't clean right away but appeared to have dropped all the cleanings/placenta at two days fresh.

Environment: Bedding used in calving area box stall barn is straw.

Observable Signs: A slight white discharge buildup on the upper tail. Some straw is stuck to it.

Physical Exam Findings: Nothing remarkable systemically. However, on rectal palpation, the uterus feels somewhat enlarged for the time since fresh.

Barn Diagnosis: Pyometra, a bacterial uterine infection.

Initial Treatment: Infuse the uterine environment to cleanse the area. Use the botanical liquid mixture of Utresept with aloe (one-part Utresept to five-parts of aloe). Infuse 60cc-120cc of the mix. Re-infuse daily for three days total treatment.

Follow-up: Homeopathic pulsatilla homeochord (multi-potency) twice daily for five days, then Silica 30C twice daily for three days.

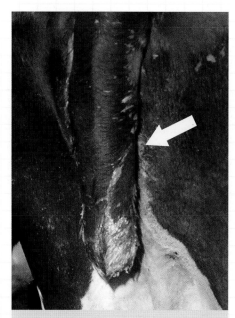

Dried "glaze" on lowest area of tail (docked) should raise suspicion of possible low grade uterine infection.

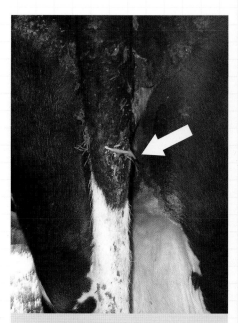

Dried glaze; noticed due to straw stuck on cow's tail at glaze.

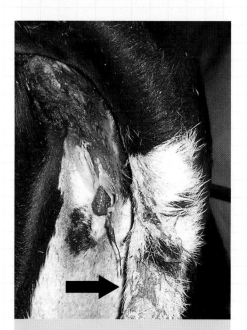

Cow with long standing severe pyometra (a couple gallons of pus in uterus). Surprisingly little discharge on tail — but the dried streaks such raise suspicion. She wasn't coming into heat and the farmer wanted to know why.

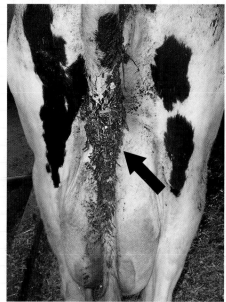

Obvious build-up on tail should raise suspicion about uterine infection.

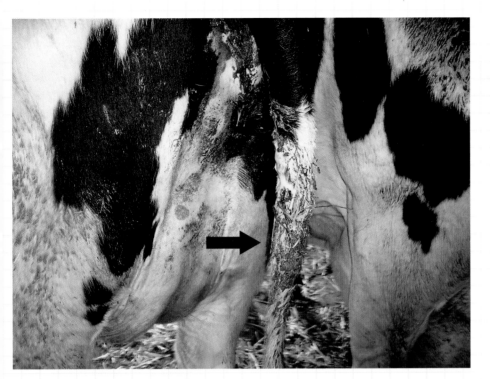

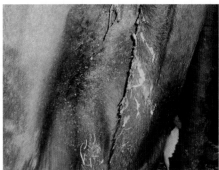

Dried glaze on tail. Black colored tails are more difficult to see contrasts with discharges.

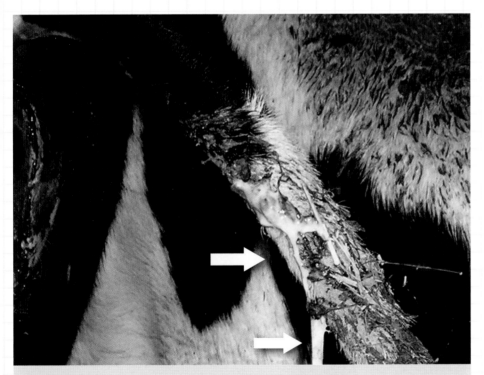

Two pictures of a cow with pus discharge, one month after calving. The picture below clearly shows the pus on the tail head that may be missed without observing closely.

The Vet Said That the Uterus is Stuck to the Rumen

Signalment: Second calf Holstein fresh about six weeks.

History/Onset: The cow had a hard calving and the farmer had been infusing her early on to keep the infection down. The discharge had stopped. The cow seemed a bit slow, however. She's doing fine now as far as eating and milk production.

Environment: Normally scheduled day for reproductive work for the herd by the herd veterinarian.

Physical Exam Findings: No physical exam was done, just the rectal exam of the cow, which showed an adhesion between the uterus and the rumen. The rest of the uterus felt to be flexible and not filled with infection. Only a certain area of the left horn was attached to the rumen at this point.

Barn Diagnosis: Peritonitis, localized.

Initial Treatment: If you can give the cow five months of time, these problems usually will resolve by then. Using homeopathic Silica 200C once daily for a few weeks may help. But in all the cases of these I've seen, it is only at about five months fresh that the cow will have normal uterine motility. The prognosis for these cows is much better if they show heats every three weeks, since the uterus contracts and moves during heat and will slowly work its way free over a few months time.

Follow-up: Just check her at each normally scheduled reproduction check over the next few months.

Considerations: This condition usually occurs due to an infusion rod piercing through the uterus. The farmer needs to be taught how to infuse properly prior to ever doing this. Farmers which already do their own artificial insemination will know how to infuse quite well. Another reason for this condition, though more rare, is due to peri-metritis. This is when there is a very bad uterine infection right after calving and the walls of the uterus can not contain all the infected material, which then seeps through the walls and creates a localized intra-abdominal peritonitis, most often at the rumen uterine area.

PROBLEM: REPRODUCTIVE ISSUES

Hasn't Shown a Heat Since About 40 Days in Milk & Now Fresh More Than Four Months

Signalment: Second lactation Holstein, fresh about 140 days.

History/Onset: She has been milking really well and was in negative energy condition during her peak milk production. She did show a heat at about 40 days in milk, but not since. The farmer didn't want to breed her then as his voluntary wait period is 60 days.

Environment: Wintertime in the barn and wintertime feeding of stored feeds.

Observable Signs: No heats shown, there is nothing wrong to all outward appearances.

Physical Exam Findings: On rectal palpation, there is a corpus luteum (CL) on one ovary and a small follicle on the other. The cow's uterus feels normal.

Barn Diagnosis: Anestrous (no heats).

Initial Treatment: Give phyto-estrogenic botanical compounds like Heat Seek. Heat Seek tablets have been used since the late 1990s and will help cows show behavioral heat

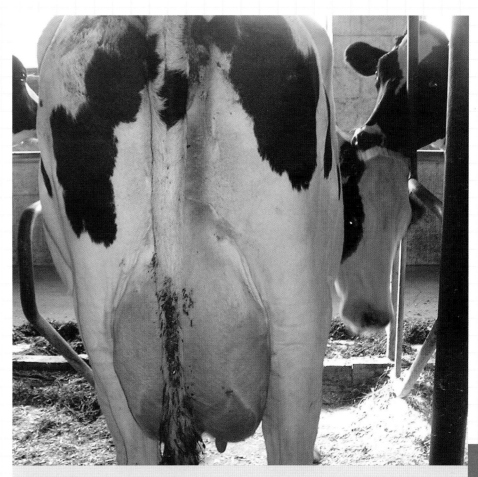

Cows that are in heat and in a tie-stall will often look back at you after reaching in rectally.

that have normal ovarian structures and normal body condition (not skinny cows). Give two tablets orally every day for six days in a row. If the cow shows a heat prior to the end of treatment time, breed and give no more of the tablets.

Follow-up: Watch for signs of heat, no matter how minor (holds milk up, doesn't quite finish her feed since she has other things on her mind, simply looks back at you an extra while). Cows on the Heat Seek treatment tend to show heats very obviously. Occasionally they will show an even stronger heat three weeks later. If so, simply re-breed.

Considerations: This herd has experienced a lot of this problem. Also, the cows do tend to show a heat around 40-50 days, but then really get into producing peak milk and always seem to breed back late. It would be good to breed the cows at 40-50 days fresh in this case and accept a slightly lower milk production but know the cow is bred. "Dr. Green" usually remedies this situation — once the grazing season starts, cows will start to show heats again. The Heat Seek does *not* work like PGF$_{2\,alpha}$ and will not dump out a bad uterus. Cows bred on a heat induced by Heat Seek tend to settle well.

PROBLEM: NEWBORN ISSUES

Intestines Extruded From Navel in Calf That is 15 Minutes Old

Signalment: Newborn, within the hour. Not yet standing but washed off by mother cow.

History/Onset: As above.

Environment: Anywhere, anytime.

Observable Signs: Intestinal loops visualized.

Physical Exam Findings: Determine whether or not the intestinal loops are completely exposed to the outside world or are still protected by layer of peritoneum (looks like they are nicely enveloped in a thin, transparent sack, see photo).

Barn Diagnosis: Prolapsed intestines.

Initial Treatment: If still in the peritoneal sack, wash the protective layer *very* gently and carefully. Have two people hold legs of calf and have third person very carefully work the sack back in through the navel. Place one to two stitches the close the navel.

Follow-up: Penicillin, 10cc twice daily for five days.

Considerations: The contamination of the peritoneal sack from the outside world will lead to massive infection once the sack is replaced into the body. Animals, especially newborn calves, have such little capability to fight off infection that withholding penicillin would clearly be negligence.

Note: If the intestinal loops are *not* protected by the peritoneal sack (the loops are fully exposed to the outside world), the case is *hopeless* due to massive contamination *and* the peritoneal layer has been ripped open haphazardly. The cause for this condition is not exactly known but one reason could be that the mother cow, when washing and stimulating the calf, may have tugged at the navel area too hard and opened it up essentially creating a hernia, allowing the intestines to come through.

Herniated intestines still in the peritoneal sack. After gentle washing and replacement, a stitch was placed to close the navel opening, and penicillin was immediately started.

One week later, the calf is completely normal and standing happily.

Three-Day-Old Calf That Started Great — Now Has Sunken Eyes, Bloat, Gray Mucus From Rectum

Three-day-old calf started great and has gone downhill quickly. Calf can no longer rise, ears are down and a moderate bloat is present.

Signalment: Three-day-old Holstein calf.

History/Onset: Calf drank quite well from its mother the first day, second day not as interested in feeding and third day is down and depressed.

Environment: In its own enclosure separate from other calves.

Observable Signs: Sunken eyes, mild bloat appearance on side of rumen, and a gray mucous coming from the rectum.

Physical Exam Findings: Increased heart rate, lungs raspy, temperature 102.8 F (39.3 C).

Barn Diagnosis: Atresia coli or atresia ani; it doesn't really matter which as they are both fatal without proper surgical correction ($$). Basically, somewhere in the calf's intestines, colon or anus there is a stricture which is causing a complete blockage, thus building up toxins which would normally be eliminated.

Initial Treatment: Surgical correction or euthanize.

Follow-up: Attentive care post surgical correction of rectum and/or colon.

Considerations: Pedigree Holsteins are known to sometimes produce a calf that has an incompletely developed colon or no anal opening at all (atresia ani). These are congenital abnormalities. That a temperature could be taken indicates that there is an opening. The grey discharge is only being produced by the colon in the section behind the blockage. The history/onset and visible signs are typical for such a calf.

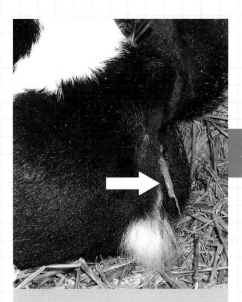

Only some mucus is being excreted from the rectum. Hopeless case. Happens in Holsteins the most.

PROBLEM: CALF DIGESTION

Diarrhea

Signalment: Jersey calf 10 days old.

History/Onset: Calf was born normally, was seen having its colostrum when it was with its mom for the first day. In the last two days, it slowed down drinking from the bottle and now can't suck well from the nipple, won't finish its bottle and has obvious diarrhea.

Environment: Calves are in individual hutches after being removed from their mother (within first 24 hours).

Observable Signs: Lies down a little more than the others its age, yellowish pasty diarrhea seen stuck to its tail and also passes diarrhea frequently.

Physical Exam Findings: Temperature is 103 F (39.4 C), lungs are clear, heart is normal, no bloating noticed, has a suck reflex when a thumb is offered, but it is not very strong. Eyebrow pinch test is positive for dehydration. Is lying down during the physical examination and doesn't get up but can hold its head up on its own.

Barn Diagnosis: Rota-corona virus or colibacillosis (coliform).

Initial Treatment: Fluid therapy. Give IV fluids if it will not suck a bottle. Tube feed four times daily until it can suck again (not just the twice a day feeding since it is losing fluids from diarrhea bouts frequently). IV fluids: 800cc lactated ringers solution, 100cc dextrose and 100cc sodium bicarbonate. Oral fluids (tube feed if needed) should be electrolytes alternating with real milk. Hyperimmune plasma (Plasma Gold or Bovi-Sera) is very indicated for this and should be given IV 100-250cc. Give 1cc Immunoboost and 3cc/100lbs. BoSe as well. Ferro, 5cc orally, once daily will help constipate the calf and also build up her blood with iron and other minerals. Ferro cannot be placed in milk.

Follow-up: Fluids, fluids, fluids! Consider homeopathic Podophyllum, Arsenicum, Merc Corr, or a coliform nosode.

Considerations: If this is continually happening and a pattern is noticed where animals are OK for a few days and then at a certain time they break with diarrhea, give 1cc of Immunoboost and BoSe right at birth to counteract the natural immune suppression that occurs then. Also consider vaccinating the dry cows about two to three weeks prior to birth with ScourGuard 4KC or the Endovac-Bovi or J-Vac (follow box directions.).

PROBLEM: CALF DIGESTION

Bloated & Standing Still

Signalment: A pre-weaned calf about two months old.

History/Onset: The calf has been normal until after the morning feeding; she is now bloated.

Environment: Individual feeding of milk replacer to calves.

Observable Signs: Standing still and obviously bloated.

Physical Exam Findings: Bloated animals don't need a full physical exam; they need to be de-bloated as fast as possible.

Barn Diagnosis: Bloat due to maldigestion of milk replacer.

Initial Treatment: Pass tube to debloat as these are free-gas bloat situations. Pump in a 8-16 oz. of mineral oil after releasing the trapped gas. This will lubricate the gut to move.

Follow-up: Feed whole milk! It is truly amazing that by mimicking mother nature (whole milk), digestive problems in calves are virtually non-existent, except for overwhelming challenges from bacteria and viruses in animals with poor immune systems.

Considerations: Individual calves can become real problems if they are not taken off of milk replacer and given whole milk. Adding hay to the diet will also reduce this problem since the rumen *muscles* will develop more quickly.

PROBLEM: CALF EXTERNAL ISSUES

Broke its Leg

Signalment: Calf born within the last two or three weeks.

History/Onset: The owner noticed the calf holding up leg a couple hours ago.

Environment: Calves are allowed to run with cows.

Observable Signs: Calf holds leg entirely off ground. Will not place any weight on it whatsoever.

Physical Exam Findings: Once caught, it is easy to feel the area of the break. The calf withdrawals leg in pain when being checked. *It is extremely important to verify if the skin has been broken or not.*

Barn Diagnosis: Fracture.

Initial Treatment: There are various ways to deal with fractures in young animals. Fortunately, young animals heal quickly if the leg is set correctly. One easy method is to use a length of PVC pipe that is vertically cut for the length needed. The idea for setting any broken limb is to immobilize the joint above and the joint below the problem area and that no movement upon that area is occurring, otherwise healing will not occur. Once the long "U" shaped PVC is cut (and filed at the ends to reduce sharp edges), place upon the broken leg and insert cotton into the area of the splint that needs to be filled in. Then use Elastikon to wrap the splint. Wrap it liberally, using two or three Elastikon rolls.

Calf with broken ankle due to hard pull by farmer at birth. You must immobilize the joint above and below the break. In this case a simple long U-shaped piece of PVC was placed behind the leg to support it, then cotton was liberally inserted to cushion the leg, and then a few rolls of Elasticon kept it in place. The cast is left on for four to five weeks.

Same calf as above immediately after cast removal. The obvious excessive angle to the ankle corrected with exercise over time.

Follow-up: Monitor the splinted leg over the next four weeks. If needing re-wrap, do so very carefully. Most often the splint stays put. It takes four or five weeks for a calf leg to heal. Giving Symphytum officinale (Comfrey, "bone knit") is advocated by many.

Heifer with broken ankle. Flies gathering nearby a suspected tiny cut (dark spot) guided the decision for immediate slaughter, since gangrene would likely set in once a cast would be applied (low oxygen to infected area).

Broken ankle up close (inset) to show the skin break and open area.

Considerations: The larger the animal, the harder to deal with a broken leg. I have successfully splinted a leg of an animal weighing about 800 lbs. The key is always to immobilize the joint above and below the break. Also, it is extremely critical to make sure that a compound fracture hasn't occurred (when the bone is exposed through the skin). These will not heal in farm animals, even the smallest ones, since clostridial gangrene is highly likely once the cast is placed (due to low oxygen to the area).

PROBLEM: CALF EXTERNAL ISSUES

Swelling on Jaw

Signalment: Three-week-old calf.

History/Onset: Presented for disbudding of horn buds; farmer said the swelling was there for maybe a week or so but it didn't hinder the calf any so he didn't think about it much.

Environment: Something that can prick the soft area of the mouth has been ingested or chewed upon (wood, stemmy forage, straw bedding).

Observable Signs: Soft, well defined swelling on the jaw or just behind it.

Physical Exam Findings: Nothing out of the ordinary except the observable sign.

Barn Diagnosis: Abscess.

Initial Treatment: These tend to resolve on their own (they spontaneously open up at some point). However, the ones that are behind the jaw and located near the top of the throat can eventually cause big problems (impeding breathing due to size) since there is essentially nothing stopping their enlargement (whereas on the jaw these seem to be limited to growth since they will burst open). Some will burst open when handling the calf for disbudding. Homeopathic Hepar Sulph 10X three times daily for 7-10 days may help the abscess open up.

Cheek swelling that will likely open on own.

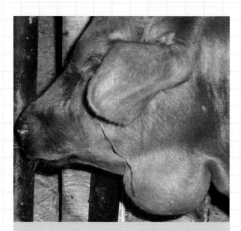
Cheek swelling that may enlarge further and then impede breathing.

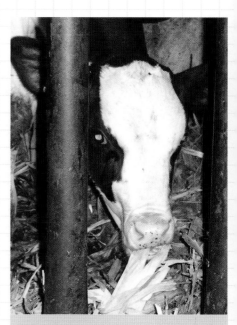
This calf is eating its bedding. Why? It might not be being fed any hay and is desperate to seek out fiber to satisfy its instinctive craving for fiber to help develop the rumen muscles. On rare occasion if a calf ingests this large a feed stuff, it may become lodged partially down the throat and cause the animal to stop eating normally. By careful inspection, these can be reached and pulled out of the throat.

Follow-up: Monitor. If the increase in size is obvious and not seeming to stop — especially for those at the top of the throat — have vet open the abscess to drain and flush. There are a lot of blood vessels nearby so don't attempt this on your own. Flushing with hydrogen peroxide will help clear out the area — just make sure there is a large enough exit area for the bubbles to escape or they could penetrate other internal structures (not good).

Considerations: Sometimes a calf will be nibbling its bedding in an attempt to satisfy its craving for fiber to develop the rumen if it's on a milk and grain only diet. Occasionally if fodder is being used for bedding, a calf may accidentally get a whole corn husk lodged in its throat. This will hinder normal eating and the calf will start going backwards. Careful inspection of the throat may reveal such a problem. Extract soggy corn husk and give lots of milk for the next bunch of days since the calf probably will have a sore throat from the irritation.

Odor & Drainage From One or Both Ears

Signalment: Holstein calf about one month old.

History/Onset: On whole milk, hay and grain. Had been a real greedy drinker from the bottle at feeding time.

Environment: Calf kennel with no outdoor access (no pen area that it can go into and enjoy fresh air).

Observable Signs: Calf is sitting normally upon inspection. Its ears are both held a little lower than normal with a dark blackish discharge. The eyes also have a discharge (clear).

Physical Exam Findings: Mildly foul odor from each ear with fever. No other abnormalities other than noted previously.

Barn Diagnosis: Ear infection.

Initial Treatment: Depending on alertness of animal, consider the non-antibiotic treatment of infectious disease in addition to local ear lavage with an herbal mixture of a *dilute* essential oil (all essential oils are antiseptic). The antiseptic herbal liquid mix needs to be infused into the ear, then hold the base of the ear closed and rotate gently a few times. Then allow calf to shake its head freely.

Follow-up: Repeat twice daily for four days.

Considerations: Ear infections are usually due to milk getting into the eustachian tube, which connects the throat to the ear. This case probably is this since both sides are affected and there is a history of the calf being a greedy drinker, thus increasing the likelihood of a "back flush" of milk into the ear region. On a farm which has bought in many animals, there could be a mycoplasma problem. Infected milk will then infect the calves drinking the milk. Farms with mycoplasma problems will usually have a history of calves with ear infections and joint swellings.

Ear of calf is not held quite high as other calves and has a dark blackish drainage.

Same calf as left and has drainage in other ear as well. Notice slight drainage from both eyes.

PROBLEM: CALF DIGESTION

Bloody Diarrhea after Doing Well

Signalment: One-and-a-half-month-old calf, was strong and had been doing well. On whole milk, hay and grain.

History/Onset: Started scouring a couple days ago when a pig was placed nearby.

Environment: Warm spring breezes from the south (pig is south of calf).

Observable Signs: Calf doesn't finish bottle and lays down a lot (but can still get up).

Physical Exam Findings: Fever, lungs raspy, liquid bloody diarrhea.

Barn Diagnosis: Bacterial scours (salmonella, coliform?).

Initial Treatment: IV — 250cc hyperimmune plasma (Plasma Gold or Bovi-Sera) with 2cc Immunoboost.

Follow-up: 5cc Phyto-Biotic (garlic, goldenseal, ginseng, barberry) orally three times daily. Feed elec-

Sick calf with fever and bloody diarrhea, about a month old. Next to pig, which may be carrying a germ from which the calf is not able to withstand a challenge.

trolytes three times a day. Possibly give another dose of hyperimmune plasma (Plasma Gold) under the skin the next day.

Considerations: I have seen other times when a free-running pig transmits germs to other animals in a barn situation (by "visiting" and rooting through an animal's feed). The other calves in this situation were unaffected — and none were as close to this pig as the one pictured in this case. Although the farmer was strongly advised to move the pig to reduce exposure to germs, the farmer didn't. I stopped by to check on the calf a couple of times. The day after initial treatment the calf looked good. When I checked on the calf four days later, it had died. The pig was still right there.

Swelling In Navel Area

Signalment: Calf is one to three months old.

History/Onset: Enlargement of navel area noticed for a few weeks.

Environment: Anywhere, anytime.

Observable Signs: Swelling of navel area.

Physical Exam Findings: Calf is normal other than the swelling under the belly. When feeling the swelling, try to determine if there is an abdominal ring that you can very carefully insert your finger(s) up into (calf will react). If so, it's a hernia. While trying to do this, if the calf responds *immediately* to pressure upon the swelling — and there is then no belly wall ring detected — likelihood of abscess is very high. Sometimes the navel cord can still be detected within the swelling — then it is an abscess. A true hernia will have an abdominal ring and the swelling will be able to be placed up into the belly *completely*. In any event, a person will be needed to firmly hold the calf while inspection is being done.

Barn Diagnosis: Depending on the above findings, either a hernia or navel abscess.

Initial Treatment: Hernia: Either wrap the calf with Elastikon (see photos) and repeat in 10 days or apply a clamping-type device and tighten it everyday (I don't like these). If navel abscess, cleanse the lowest area of the mass with alcohol, quickly pierce a needle into the mass to see if pus comes out. If so, use a scalpel to make an "X" to allow drainage. Cleanse with 60cc 3% hydrogen peroxide or Betadine for the first two days.

Follow-up: Keep in *very clean* area if abscess has been opened up. If hernia, re-wrap in 10 days (or when the Elastikon curls up). Hoof wrap will not work, as it is too flexible.

Considerations: Careful as there *can* be a mixed hernia and abscess situation. Sometimes it may be best to simply watch the swelling and *do nothing*. If it is a true hernia, it will continually grow as the calf grows and will look symmetrical whereas abscess situations tend to have a lopsided appearance in some minor way. This is a hereditary trait in some Holstein lines.

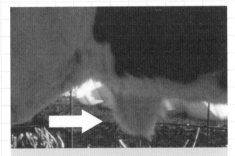

Calf with swelling at navel. If the entire mass can be gently but firmly pushed completely up into belly, then it is a hernia (and you should be able to be able to place one to two fingers up through the hernia ring. If you feel any firmness or a cord-like feel (former umbilical cord) and cannot lift it up into belly completely then it is an abscess.

Calf with hernia that got a belly wrap using two to three rolls of Elastikon (using hoof wraps will not work as they are not firm enough). The herniated area is pushed up into the belly just prior to wrapping the spot. Then keep wrapping belly to give support. Elastikon will often curl up and need to be re-wrapped a week later. Total time on calf is about two weeks. Amazingly, most hernias will be healed up by this method if the hernia ring is no bigger than two fingers wide. This is a hereditary trait in some purebred Holstein lines.

PROBLEM: CALF BREATHING

Coughing Calf/Calves

Signalment: Calves anywhere from two weeks of age and older are coughing to various degrees.

History/Onset: Started with a slight dry hacking cough a couple weeks ago. Has gotten worse and it sounds like a wet cough now. Appetite good but with the wet cough they get winded easily when they are moving around or rustled up. Disbudded recently about 10 days ago.

Environment: Damp bedding underneath new bedding that was just added. The weather has been changing, freezing at night and above freezing during the day.

Observable Signs: Variable types of coughing — some simple dry coughs to more troubling wet coughing sounds.

Physical Exam Findings: Temperature ranges from 102.8-105.6 F (39.3-40.9 C). The calves with temperatures at the low end or the very high end actually look the best. The animals with temperatures in the 103.4-104.5 F (39.7-40.3 C) mid-range appear to be worse off. Lungs range from slightly raspy to very rough with some "wet" abscess sounds and some crackles and pops. Otherwise there are no other significant findings.

Barn Diagnosis: Pneumonia, to varying degrees.

Two calves with very different response to respiratory challenge

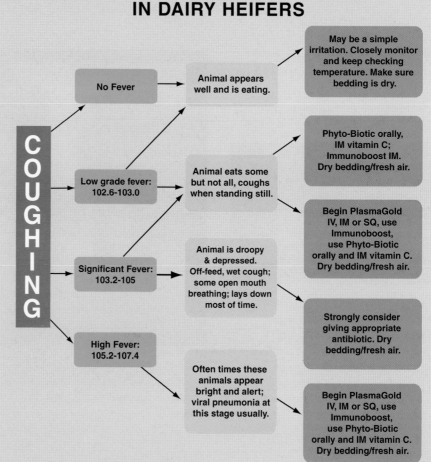

TREATING COUGHING PROBLEMS IN DAIRY HEIFERS

COUGHING

No Fever → Animal appears well and is eating. → May be a simple irritation. Closely monitor and keep checking temperature. Make sure bedding is dry.

Low grade fever: 102.6-103.0 → Animal eats some but not all, coughs when standing still. → Phyto-Biotic orally, IM vitamin C; Immunoboost IM. Dry bedding/fresh air.

→ Begin PlasmaGold IV, IM or SQ, use Immunoboost, use Phyto-Biotic orally and IM vitamin C. Dry bedding/fresh air.

Significant Fever: 103.2-105 → Animal is droopy & depressed. Off-feed, wet cough; some open mouth breathing; lays down most of time. → Strongly consider giving appropriate antibiotic. Dry bedding/fresh air.

High Fever: 105.2-107.4 → Often times these animals appear bright and alert; viral pneumonia at this stage usually. → Begin PlasmaGold IV, IM or SQ, use Immunoboost, use Phyto-Biotic orally and IM vitamin C. Dry bedding/fresh air.

Group of calves inside a cinder block building with rough hair coats and coughing. Underlying parasitism is likely cause of poor immune response to conditions (poor ventilation and damp bedding) which encourage respiratory problems.

Open mouth breathing — not a good sign as it means the animal is desperate to have the least resistance to take air in.

Initial Treatment: Put animals outside (if inside currently) to get fresh air and be away from damp bedding. Use calf jackets if necessary for warmth but get them into a *fresh* air space. Medicinal treatment strongly depends on clinical presentation. Animals, regardless of temperature, that appear fairly well and robust can be treated with natural methods. Any animal with wet abscess sounds in the lungs or is having obvious respiratory difficulty really should be put onto an antibiotic without delay to ensure proper animal welfare.

Natural treatment includes 100cc plasma therapy (Plasma Gold) under the skin or in muscle, vitamin C (5cc/100 lbs.), Phyto-Biotic orally three times a day (5-10cc), Immunoboost (1cc/200 lbs.), and BoSe (3cc/100 lbs.).

Terrible damp environment for calves. One spell of rainy, cold weather will send these calves into a respiratory condition.

Follow-up: Phyto-Biotic, 5-10cc, orally twice daily.

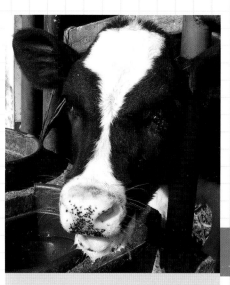

Calf with respiratory difficulty. Notice that the calf is in a "calf kennel" but has no regular access to fresh air, thus possibly contributing to the situation.

Considerations: Raise calves outside in fresh air, away from adult animals. Once calves are brought outside away from the main adult barn, they should *not* return there until they themselves are milking animals.

PROBLEM: HOOF ISSUES

Lame in Hoof with Swelling Above Hoof-Hairline Junction But Still Below the Two Dew Claws

Signalment: Any breed, any age.

History/Onset: Progressive lameness in one limb over a few days; could be rapid onset in some cases.

Environment: Any time of year but more likely when animals are going outside.

Observable Signs: Animal places limb very slightly on ground if standing still, but is obviously lame when walking.

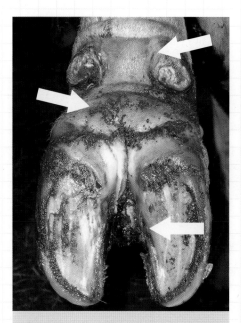

Foot rot is always between the two toes. Whenever an interdigital corn is ulcerated, foot rot is sure to follow. Notice the very inflamed purplish pink area above the hooves — this indicates infection of the entire joint.

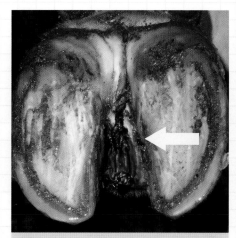

Same hoof as left. Foot rot due to ulcerated interdigital corn (cut out to get rid of problem and to bring new circulation to area).

Physical Exam Findings: Upon inspection of hoof (with animal properly restrained for careful examination), there is a slimy, foul smelling area between both toes. Looking at it closely reveals a soft, blackish area with a rip in the skin. If the hoof and animal is strongly restrained, running your finger through the area between the hooves will cause the animal to flinch. You will also extract some dead material when doing this.

Barn Diagnosis: Foot rot.

Initial Treatment: First, manually remove as much of the crud as possible. Then apply hydrogen peroxide and allow it to bubble and fizz for a good half minute or more. Then mix $1/2$ cup granular sugar with about

20cc Betadine (*not* tincture of iodine) to make a thick orange paste. Apply a good size blob of this paste to cotton and place it into the area between the toes. Wrap with a hoof wrap of your choice, making sure that the toes are spread apart with your wrapping.

Follow-up: Take off the wrap in three to four days. You will most likely see a "core" of dead material that almost falls out on its own (if not falling out, remove it manually). This is a good sign. Then cleanse with hydrogen peroxide again and apply the remainder of the sugar-Betadine mix. In three of four more days, remove the wrap and inspect. Repeat the earlier steps if needed.

Considerations: Foot rot is usually due to a puncture of some kind between the toes. Oftentimes this is due to rocks in lanes that the animals are walking on but it also may be due to brittle stubble or other items (cracked cement in the cow yard, etc.). Cattle with interdigital corns (growth between the toes) are very susceptible to foot rot if the growth is pierced or punctured. If

A foot rot case after the first wrap has been removed. A dead ropey core of cheesy tissue fell out when cleansing and revealed the above.

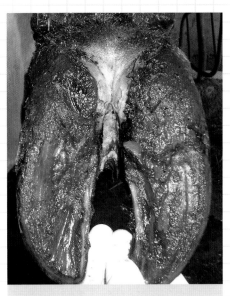

Same foot rot case as left after the second wrap was removed four days later. A very noticeable improvement is seen by smaller area and pink color. A final cleanse and wrap were applied and recovery was complete.

an interdigital growth is involved in a foot rot case, it must be cut away. This will not only get rid of the growth but also cause bleeding in the area, which is good as new circulation will help the healing process that you will start with the cleansing and wrapping procedure.

PROBLEM: HOOF ISSUES

Getting Gradually More Lame

Signalment: Any animal that is walking around.

History/Onset: The animal has likely been outside, either in pasture or in the concrete barnyard. The farmer usually sees the lameness for only a few days, but in reality it has been occurring for a longer period. This is because the bovine has two toes per limb. If one toe is injured mildly (at first), it can "hide" the problem by bearing weight on the other toe until the problem in the bad toe has festered and she can no longer hide the problem.

Environment: More often in continually damp or wet environments since the hooves will be softer and allow things to pierce the bottom of the hoof easier. However, in very dry times going out to pasture or in the pasture itself, there will be no "give" to the ground and a rock can penetrate the bottom of the hoof.

Observable Signs: When walking the cow resists placing their full weight upon the ground when the lame hoof has to bear the weight. If the condition has gone on for a long time, there will likely be rub sores on the hook bone area of the opposite side (due to not laying down on the bad side).

Physical Exam Findings: Possibly some swelling above the affected toe, but not always (depends on the length of time of the festering). The

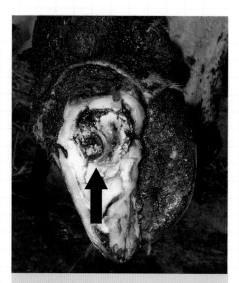

Hoof abscess pared away to show large area near heel as site of abscess.

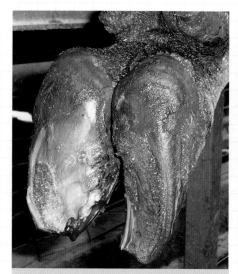

Abscess pared away at the white line area (junction of wall and sole).

limb and animal must be properly restrained and the hoof lifted for close inspection. Focus in on areas of the bottom of the hoof that have a slight bulge or bump. This is likely an area that has not been normally worn down and excess hoof growth is accumulating. Pare this area away. If a shiny black area appears, pare this area away also. Other times there will be a black line "trail" — once you have followed the black line to where it ends, this is usually where the exact spot of the abscess is. Success will be when a foul fluid is released. Sometimes there will be a "false hoof" (growth not worn down) that can be over a rather large portion of the hoof. Trim this away as it can gather dirt too easily in the future. A good rule of thumb is to trim away any excess hoof if you can place a finger between it and the true hoof underneath.

Barn Diagnosis: Hoof abscess.

Initial Treatment: Once the abscess has been located and opened up —

and open them up to *at least* the size of a quarter — cleanse the area with hydrogen peroxide and apply the sugar-Betadine wrap (described in the *Lame in Hoof with Swelling / Foot Rot case in Above Hoof*). A hoof abscess, if not opened up fully, will get worse).

Follow-up: This may or may not need to be re-wrapped in a few days.

Considerations: Lameness in the front limbs is quicker to show itself than lameness in the rear limbs. This is because a cow bears about 60 percent of its weight on the front half of the body and only 40 percent on the rear limbs. If there is a *rapid* onset of lameness, an abscess may be at the very front of a toe. Animals with black hooves have a different composition than white-hooved animals. Therefore, black-hooved animals can withstand problems more than white hoofed animals. However, working on black hooves is much more difficult and requires sharper hoof knives and nippers.

Injury at Hoof-Hairline Junction

Signalment: First calf heifer, fresh in the last few days.

History/Onset: Immediately.

Environment: Tie-stall barn with gutter grates.

Observable Signs: Animal holds its hoof off the ground immediately after having gotten her hoof stuck into the grates which she was walking parallel on.

Physical Exam Findings: Obvious injury at hoof-hairline junction. By the time the vet is called in, usually about two or three days after the injury, the swelling can be substantial.

Barn Diagnosis: Laceration (cut) at coronary band (hoof-hairline junction).

Initial Treatment: Immediately hose the area with cool or luke warm water three to four times a day for at least two or three days. Not doing this almost always leads to a severe problem since hooves tend to be in contact with manure and dirt, which will rapidly infect the area.

Follow-up: After three days, cleanse with hydrogen peroxide and then wrap with whatever healing salve you like. The Betadine sugar mix (described in the *Lame in Hoof with Swelling/Foot Rot* case) would be fine or perhaps simply calendula ointment. Change wrap *daily* for

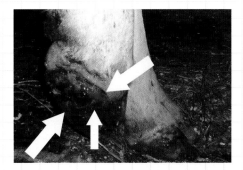

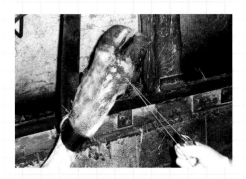
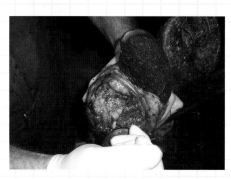

Top: Hoof-hairline injury; leg immobilized with cow on her back.
Middle: Amputation using gigli; cauterizing amputated stump.
Bottom: Betadine and sugar mix; final outcome of a successful amputation.
See page 56 for additional image descriptions.

five days minimum, gently cleaning each time.

Considerations: Unfortunately, most farmers play the "wait and see" game. In this instance, there is nothing worse than this. Cleansing from the get-go is extremely critical. Most of the time this kind of case results in amputation of the toe, if the infection has not yet affected the inner joint, as seen by obvious swelling above the hoof-hairline junction above the damaged toe. Amputation is shown in the series of photos with this case. If the veterinarian carries out an amputation of the toe, the toe will not grow back and the cow can do fine on one toe for many lactations. The farmer must commit to changing the bandage of the newly created stump *twice weekly for four weeks.* The cow in the photos went on to do well.

PROBLEM: HOOF ISSUES

Stands With Hoof Barely Touching Ground — There May Be More Than One Cow Doing This

Signalment: Any stage of lactation, any breed — but usually has white hooves.

History/Onset: Animal has been slowly getting more lame over a week or two.

Environment: Tie-stall or free stall; cows standing for periods of time in manure slop is likely; high starch ration or imbalance/deficiency of minerals.

Observable Signs: Cow tends to place only the front of the toe upon the ground and will stand in that position a lot.

Physical Exam Findings: Upon appropriate limb and animal re-straint, the problem area is quickly observed to be at the hoof-hairline junction on any limb, on any side (front, back or edge) of the hoof. The rear limbs are more commonly af-fected. The area may be a hollowed out or plump (like a strawberry) area. It is usually covered by a thin dry layer (scab).

Unwashed hairy heel wart at hoof-hairline junction (1).

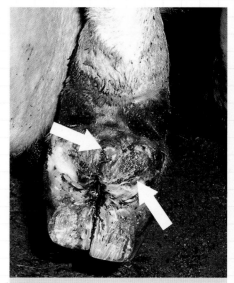

Hairy heel wart pared — notice it is affecting both sides of the heel (2).

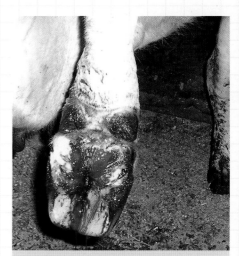

Hairy heel wart pared and washed (3).

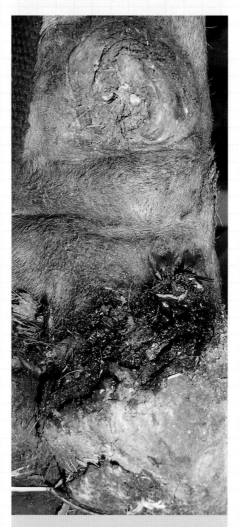

Typical site of a hairy heel wart at hoof-hairline junction.

Barn Diagnosis: Hairy heel wart/strawberry heel.

Initial Treatment: The dry layer that covers over the active lesion must be removed. With proper restraint of animal and limb, scuff off the layer or use a well-sharpened hoof knife and carefully (but quickly) peel it off. Do *not* go deeply as there are blood vessels nearby — just get the dried layer off. If no dry layer is present (only the active moist lesion), still pare off the most surface layer. The animal will definitely dislike the procedure. *But* — once the surface layer is off, almost anything will work for a wrap. This is because the problem is much like poison ivy — only on the surface. Once the active area is removed, you will also find the animal does not mind being touched there. But before then, it is very painful. Cleanse with hydrogen peroxide and apply the sugar and Betadine mix as described in the *Lame in Hoof with Swelling/Foot Rot* case.

Follow-up: Sometimes these need to be re-wrapped, other times not. Monitor and use common sense.

Considerations: There is likely a nutritional component to this problem. It is interesting that this problem seems to have really taken hold once rations became higher in starch (for milk production). If so, the effects of subacute rumen acidosis could be affecting general hoof health. Since the hoof-hairline junction *is* a very delicate area as far as circulation is concerned, any upset of circulation in that area could easily make for an impaired structure, thereby allowing the germs (if present) to take hold. Then the rest of the problem starts. This would be the case on farms that have a relatively high starch level of feeding ("hot" rations). On the other hand, farms that are not delivering sufficient mineral intake or out of balance minerals could also find this problem due to impaired hoof health and growth. This is more likely the case on grazing farms that may apply very minimal inputs into the system.

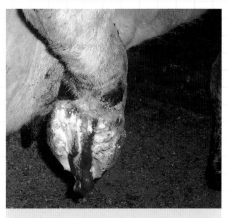

Hydrogen peroxide fizzing action upon what was hairy heel wart (4).

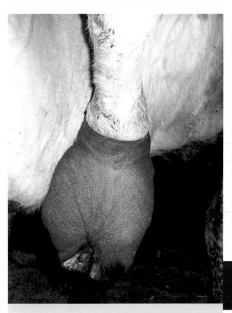

Hairy heel wart wrapped with Betadine and sugar mix on cotton below hoof wrap (5).

Swollen Back Leg and Lame But Bears Weight Fully

Signalment: Second lactation Holstein-Jersey mix, fresh three months.

History/Onset: Over the last three weeks a bulge has been noticed on the flank in front of the right hind leg.

Environment: Grazing dairy, but cows are on a concrete cow yard a lot since it is just prior to grazing season.

Observable Signs: Cow eats normally and milks normally. She is short strided in the right hind limb but plants full weight on the ground.

Physical Exam Findings: Cleansed and scrubbed the swelling on the flank. With cow restrained and someone pushing up on her tail, an IV (14 gauge) needle was thrust into the swelling and pus immediately came out.

Barn Diagnosis: Abscess.

Initial Treatment: Find the weakest spot on the swelling but always try to open a spot that is lowest to the ground to encourage better drainage by gravity after initial flushing. Open abscess with an "X" incision with a scalpel blade. We drained out

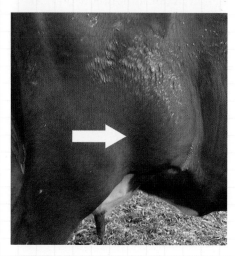

Abscess on flank, tapped, opened up and drained.

a gallon or more of pus. The hollowed out pocket was flushed liberally with hydrogen peroxide and on the last flush used chlorhexidine.

Follow-up: Repeat hydrogen peroxide flush at least twice daily for next two days. Then stop.

Considerations: Occasionally a flank swelling will be an accumulation of blood. Tapping the swelling is necessary prior to opening it up further for drainage (if abscess) since a hematoma (blood accumulation) will bleed continuously and need stitches to stop the bleeding, if opened up in error. Additionally, the location shown in the photos is

where the prefemoral lymph node is located. A lymph node will feel firm, however. For the abscess discussed above, there may be a "core" of dried pus that develops in a few days, hindering drainage. This should be pulled out and the hollow pocket re-flushed. During fly season, some sort of fly repellent should be applied to the area.

PROBLEM: HOOF ISSUES

Swelling at the Outside Area of the Hock

Signalment: Lactating cow of any age.

History/Onset: The swelling has slowly increased over many weeks.

Environment: Tie-stall.

Observable Signs: Obvious swelling on the outside area of the hock.

Physical Exam Findings: Nothing remarkable except for the swelling, and it doesn't seem to bother the animal too much.

Barn Diagnosis: Hock swelling.

Initial Treatment: Not treatable — and do *not* try to lance the swelling as it is almost never an abscess. Lancing the area will create a much worse situation since you will likely open up the joint capsule, which should never be exposed to the outside environment.

Follow-up: Lack of bedding is the reason for this problem. Therefore increase bedding or install "mattresses" of high quality (Petersheim mattresses, etc.).

Considerations: If the swelling is very infected (see photo with this case), there is almost no hope for such a situation. The animal seen in the top photo will likely become normal (or at least decrease the swell-

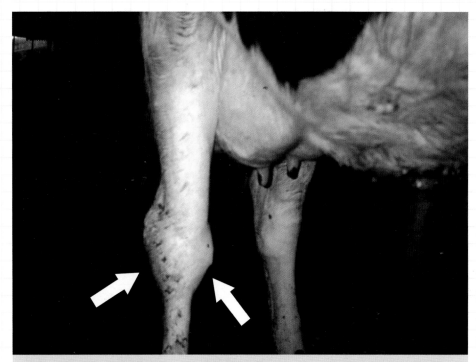

Complete hock swelling, on both inside and outside of hock. This is generally worse for the cow than a swelling just on the outside.

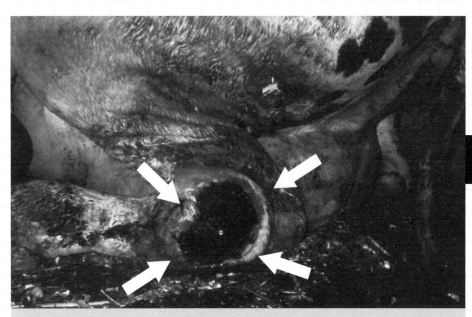

Very infected hock (purple around black central area).

ing size) after mattresses are installed. I have seen a bull that lived in a clean, well-bedded box stall that had a permanent swelling on each of the hocks and not infected — most likely genetic.

Increased Thickening of Leg Between Two Joints & is Lame

Signalment: Any breed, any time of life.

History/Onset: Farmer noticed that the cow was not bearing weight on the front limb as well as was done normally and laid down more and more over the last week.

Environment: Tie-stall with curbing in front of animals to separate feed manger from stall.

Observable Signs: Thickening of the straight bone between the ankle and knee of front leg.

Physical Exam Findings: Cow was slightly slow on finishing her feed and has a low-grade fever; otherwise nothing abnormal beyond the swelling. A low-grade fever is present.

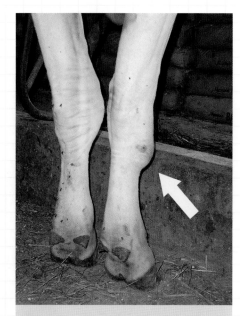

Animal recovered from cellulitis without using antibiotics. Notice the original spot of initial infection.

Barn Diagnosis: Cellulitis.

Initial Treatment: If an opening is observed where the infection point may have started and if there is some drainage point below that area, consider flushing from the top with a hyperimmune plasma (Plasma Gold or Bovi-Sera). Give animal IV vitamin C and dextrose with 90cc Phyto-Biotic (garlic, goldenseal, ginseng, barberry mix).

Follow-up: Follow-up with Phyto-Biotic orally, 20cc twice daily for four days.

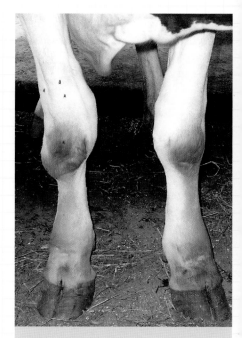

Same animal as left — only a slightly larger joint is evidence of any previous problem. The animal bore weight fully on the limb.

Considerations: As noted in the lumpy jaw section, if there is a cellulitis occurring and its spread can be contained between two joints, there is hope for a non-antibiotic treatment to be successful. However, if the cellulitis is located in an area where it can rapidly spread without any areas to block its spread, consider antibiotics.

PROBLEM: LEG ISSUES

Swollen Thigh & Has Quickly Gone Off-Feed

Signalment: Any age, anytime, but usually an adult.

History/Onset: Rapid (within last six to eight hours). Farmer had given an intramuscular shot into the back of the leg that day.

Environment: Any, but some farms are more prone than others (depending on geographic location).

Observable Signs: Swollen leg.

Physical Exam Findings: Cow has a low-grade fever, the leg is swollen and feels "crackly" in certain spots when touched and squeezed a little.

Barn Diagnosis: Blackleg.

Initial Treatment: Penicillin immediately and/or IV antibiotics. Making some slices into the swollen area may help release some of the gas forming.

Follow-up: If the animal lives through the end of the day, continue on antibiotics.

Considerations: While this is a rare and sporadic problem in the eastern United States, areas of the western and midwestern U.S. are known as blackleg areas. The germ that causes the condition is a clostridial organism, which can be effectively prevented by vaccination but are often deadly if clinical disease arises.

PROBLEM: LEG ISSUES

Long Bone in Leg is Exposed Due to Injury

Signalment: Any animal, anytime.

History/Onset: The injury is obvious, once observed.

Environment: Anywhere. Perhaps more so if there is crowding and an animal cannot properly get proper footing and/or if there is a lot of large, solid junk in the area.

Observable Signs: The white of the bone will be showing, with or without swelling of flesh around it. The length of time between injury and detection or between injury and addressing it will determine swelling.

Physical Exam Findings: Be extremely careful when examining the area; the animal will likely really let it fly if you walk right up to it and try to feel it.

Barn Diagnosis: Exposed bone with or without infection.

Initial Treatment: It is absolutely critical to keep the wound clean, especially if found immediately. Sedation and analgesia are likely needed to be able to work on the area. Dy's Liquid Bandage has worked on one particularly bad injury when it was

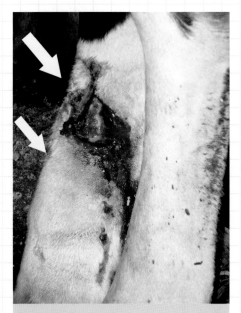

Serious infection let go too long (neglect) — notice the dried area of skin and swelling below the exposed bone (compare to other leg on same animal).

addressed immediately (see photo of healed exposed bone in infection).

Follow-up: Re-wrap every couple of days.

Considerations: If this kind of injury is not addressed immediately, it *will* become infected. At this point no antibiotic will work either. Bone infections are some of the most difficult to deal with, whether they are right on the surface or deeper in. In humans, IV antibiotics are normally needed for successful outcome. In the photo of the healed exposed bone infection, it was summertime and maggots were found after the third change of bandage. This normally is a bad sign. However, occasionally, maggots can be "good" as they will eat flesh that is dead. So

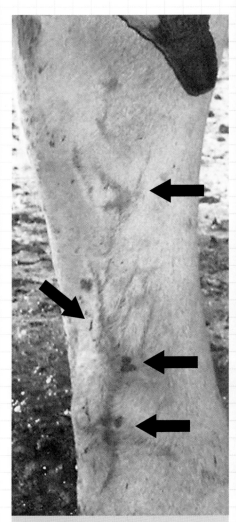

Healed exposed bone infection. Excellent care and conscientious involvement of extra labor to keep area clean is critical for positive outcome. Scar line indicated. Different animal than shown to left.

in a very, very limited manner, the maggots actually helped the animal in this case. Interestingly, maggots are used in human medicine in very specific and limited ways (just as leeches are used to reduce areas of blood buildup).

PROBLEM: BREATHING ISSUES

Breathing a Bit Quicker & Coughs — Just Fresh First Calf Heifer

Signalment: First calf heifer, fresh six days.

History/Onset: Uneventful calving, started well but now symptoms have started in last 24-48 hours.

Environment: Tie-stall barn in wintertime; heifer had been outside with other dry cows and bred heifers until calving day.

Observable Signs: Fur looks damp, maybe even sweaty, perhaps hair is up on end or "curly" looking; breathing is increased and shallow (as seen by watching rib cage), some dry coughing is heard occasionally.

Physical Exam Findings: Temperature is 103.8 F (39.9 C), lungs are rough and raspy, heart rate is increased to about 90 beats per minute, rumen is OK, udder is OK on CMT, uterus is fine as she passed her placenta right after calving.

Barn Diagnosis: Pneumonia

Initial Treatment: IV 250cc hyperimmune plasma (Plasma Gold), 5cc Immunoboost, 90cc Phyto-Biotic tincture (garlic, goldenseal, ginseng, and barberry) added to 500cc dextrose, 250-500cc vitamin C.

Follow-up: 20cc Phyto-Biotic orally twice daily for four days; *fresh air.*

Considerations: This condition is almost entirely seen in tie-stall barns in the wintertime when a heifer is stressed from calving, mixed in with animals, and there is relatively stale air (compared to where she was outside). Vaccinating with the intranasal vaccine (TSV-2 or Nasalgen) about four days prior to entry into the barn is highly effective.

The intranasal vaccines are excellent at preventing pneumonia and should be used when moving animals or commingling animals. Give it about four to five days prior to movement if possible.

PROBLEM: BREATHING ISSUES

Breathing Hard, Looks Anxious

Signalment: Second calf Holstein, fresh about two weeks.

History/Onset: Cow was slow to start and the farmer had used some supplements. In the last two days he had been drenching the cow with 4-8 ounces of a homemade herbal tea, hoping to get her started.

Environment: Anytime/anywhere.

Observable signs: Cow coughs and looks anxious. Shallow quick breathing is noticed. Hair looks a bit sweaty and is up on end.

Physical Exam Findings: Temp. 104.5 F (40.5 C), increased respiratory frequency with shallow breaths, heart rate increased, rumen working, no pings, udder OK on CMT, uterus OK (cow cleaned right after calving), eyes are a bit sunk. When listening to the lungs, all sorts of sounds are heard — crackles, wheezes, liquids, and air pipe sounds.

Barn Diagnosis: Aspiration pneumonia, due to drenching of liquid into the lungs.

Initial Treatment: These are very difficult cases because there should *never, ever* be anything in the lungs besides air. There really is no treatment unfortunately. Antibiotics won't even solve the problem because they only work on bacteria. The lungs are filled with foreign liquids.

Follow-up: Emergency salvage.

Considerations: I always feel bad in these cases since there really is nothing that can be done. The farmer isn't happy and the cow is obviously suffering. I have never liked the idea of drenching cows as this kind of problem will almost always happen at least once to farmers that routinely drench cows. It kind of comes down to the volume used. If the volume is less than 30cc at any time, it probably is OK. But when using a caulking size tube gun of thick oozing liquid there is 300cc in that one container. Using a soda or wine bottle also delivers about the same amount of volume. Drenching a cow can be done *if* the head is held about level to the ground and the cow is allowed to decide to swallow or spit out the liquid being given — not just mindlessly letting the liquid flow into the cows mouth.

Usually people will tell me they noticed the cow thrashing about when they drenched them. If so, listen to the cow! Stop what you're doing. The time the cow was thrashing while being drenched was the moment that the fluid was going into the lungs. Also, never, *ever* hold a cow's head so its nose is to the sky while drenching. This is the easiest way to get things into the lungs.

A far better way than the drenching method is to use a stomach pump system. These can be bought for between $100-$300 and allow for correct placement of tube, such that the lungs are not damaged. In general, *always pass the tube under the left nostril of the cow or calf* (if the cows head is pointing forward from you). The esophagus (throat) is always collapsed until food or something is being swallowed. Therefore, you should not get any air if you suck back upon the tube as it is being passed down the cow's throat. If you can suck back air, you are in the trachea (windpipe), which is rigid, and goes to the lungs.

The trachea runs down the right side of the neck (Thus pass the tube left of center, under the left nostril area, into the cow's mouth). Once the tube is into the rumen, you will hear sounds and if you smell the tube, it should smell somewhat of cud. *Knowing how to pass a tube is a powerful tool as a herdsman.* It will also allow you to de-bloat an animal that needs it.

PROBLEM: BREATHING ISSUES

Started Slow; Eats Some & "Breathes Funny" — Older Cow Fresh One Week

Signalment: Older cow, fresh one week.

History/Onset: Started slow, eats some, "breathes funny."

Environment: Tie-stall barn, winter feeding and cows are inside most of the time.

Observable Signs: Fluid buildup at udder and milk veins is prominent. Fluid buildup behind each jaw is noticeable as well.

Physical Exam Findings: On exam (four to five days after signs started) cow has a snoring sound every time she exhales — but can only be heard with a stethoscope; heart is difficult to hear (muffled) but normal otherwise. Has odd soft swellings below ears near neck. Brisket area between her front legs is somewhat enlarged.

Barn Diagnosis: Heart disease giving fluid retention along with strong respiratory component.

Initial Treatment: Reduce fluid retention — give diuretics. Give IV Plasma Gold or Bovi-Sera, Phyto-Biotic in dextrose and vitamin C, flunixin and furosemide. Magnet.

Follow-up: Flunixin IM and furosemide IM.

Considerations: Two days later: not much better but no worse. May want to consider switching to an antibiotic to give better chance of survival, and then ship the cow for beef in a few weeks.

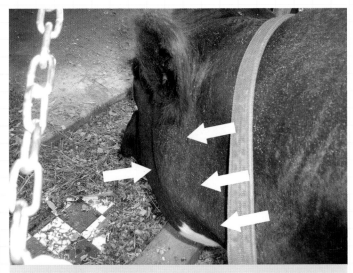

Swelling just behind the jaw (in front of collar) along with thickened jugular vein (seen at low area of neck behind collar).

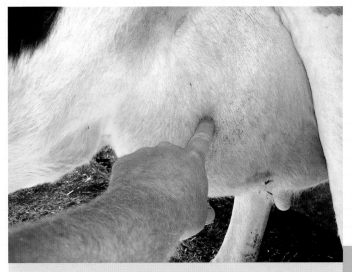

Edema as shown by pushing a finger into the area and seeing if an indentation remains afterwards. Udder edema is most common in freshening heifers; it can be severe and lead to very poor circulation and possibly gangrene in extreme cases.

Foul Smelling Nasal Discharge & Swelling Slightly Below & Including Eye

Signalment: Any age, any breed.

History/Onset: The farmer has noticed the cow eating less over the last few days and an odor when he is feeding her.

Environment: Anytime, anywhere.

Observable Signs: The cow's eye is slightly swollen, there is swelling of the nose in front and slightly below eye. Slightly reddish, thickened nasal discharge. Cow is slightly off-feed.

Physical Exam Findings: Low-grade fever, rumen OK, no twisted stomach, heart rate slightly elevated (due to fever), lungs clear, the uterus is OK, the left kidney is normal size, the udder feels normal and has a regular CMT. The eye is swollen and looks halfway shut, with a thickening or swelling of the area below it. The nasal discharge on the same side of the swelling smells foul.

Barn Diagnosis: Sinusitis, possibly due to a tooth root abscess or a fractured facial bone (due to trauma).

Initial Treatment: IV 250cc hyper-immune plasma (Plasma Gold or Bovi-Sera), 5cc Immunoboost, 90cc antibacterial tincture (Phyto-Biotic) in 500cc bottle of dextrose, 500cc vitamin C.

Follow-up: 20-30cc Phyto-Biotic orally twice daily for 7-10 days.

Considerations: If the follow-up treatment is not done for a long enough time, the original symptoms will return. If so, switch to an antibiotic as these infections are in an area where there is not good circulation (which means the immune system cannot reach it well).

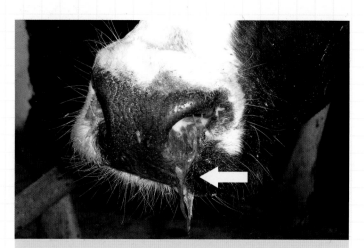

Notice the reddish tinge to the discharge. It was also foul smelling.

Same animal as the left, notice the bulge on the face bone. It is an infection, possibly due to sinusitis, tooth root abscess or trauma. Also notice the semi-closed eye due to the bone swelling.

PROBLEM: OFF-FEED ISSUES

Fresh a Few Days, Generally Quiet, Not Eating Much

Signalment: Third lactation Holstein, fresh four days.

History/Onset: The cow calved in on her own overnight four days ago and passed the placenta by morning — by the time the farmer had come out to milk. The calf is fine, a nice heifer that eats and drinks well. The farmer has given the cow some IV dextrose and calcium one time. She also has given direct fed microbials for a couple days.

Environment: Anytime, anywhere.

Observable signs: The cow appears normal but hasn't been interested in eating much. She hasn't really bagged up (udder filled up). She seems generally "quiet." She is not interactive with other animals but she is not obviously ill.

Physical Exam Findings: CMT (California mastitis test) is fine for all four quarters, heart rate is slow normal, lungs are difficult to hear any air movement, rumen is very slow, no pings (no twist) and no pongs on the right (slow gut), uterus is OK since she cleaned on time after calving, there is a golden thick mucous plug from the cervix, hydration by eyebrow pinch test shows mild dehydration. On rectal palpation, there seems to be a bit more "space" than usual and a kidney has some small air bubbles surrounding it. *When feeling the skin over the backbone area, there is a crackly feel to it when squeezed.* This is detected only on one side of the backbone and actually extends a little bit down towards the shoulder blade and neck.

Barn Diagnosis: Ruptured lung.

Initial Treatment: Unfortunately there is no real effective treatment for this condition. Why? Because every time the animal breathes, there is a small escape of air via the lung rupture to the rest of the body internally, which makes its way upwards — since air is a gas. Probably the best treatment would be to ship the cow for salvage sooner rather than later. A ruptured lung is a ruptured lung, obviously no longer functional.

Follow-up: While the gas in these conditions is not toxic (unlike with gangrene), the accumulation can increase to a point where the animal is quite swollen pretty quickly within a couple days.

Considerations: These cases are admittedly pretty rare, but do occur. There are lots more common cases for a cow not starting after freshening. *The cardinal sign is the crackly air along the top line and off to one side.* A cow may get a ruptured lung during calving as she strains and a weak lung area breaks. I think this is more likely in animals that may have had pneumonia earlier in life.

PROBLEM: BEHAVIOR ISSUES

Seems Hyper-Excitable (Jumpy, Touchy)

Signalment: Second-calf cow, fresh about two months.

History/Onset: The heifer was doing fine up until a day ago when she was a bit off-feed.

Environment: Springtime and the cows have recently been put out to pasture. The pasture is in a fast growth stage.

Observable Signs: It is difficult to catch the animal in a large box pen. Each time she is tentatively caught, she charges away. When finally catching her and putting a halter on, she is obviously distressed. She has been used to people for a year now since she was in the milking string. She is normally a fairly friendly cow.

Physical Exam Findings: Increased heart rate with a few irregular heart beats, lungs normal, rumen is contracting a bit more quickly than normal, no twisted stomach, the udder is normal on palpation and CMT, rectal palpation reveals nothing odd.

Barn Diagnosis: Grass tetany (low magnesium).

Initial Treatment: IV one bottle CMPK or Cal-Phos #2

Follow-up: Six magnesium oxide boluses (pink pills) twice a day, for a day or two to provide serious amounts of much needed magnesium to the system. Epsom salt in capsules will help if no pink pills are available. Pyck-Me-Up (Organic) will also help.

Considerations: Magnesium deficiency causes excitability as well as interferes with normal muscle contractions. Pastures that are growing quickly can be relatively low in magnesium and then cows may become affected. Make sure soil fertility of pastures is in balance.

PROBLEM: OFF-FEED ISSUES

Has a Slight Swelling at the Back of Her Throat

Signalment: Second lactation Holstein, fresh three weeks.

History/Onset: The farmer has been doing everything in his power to get the cow going to avoid having to call the vet. The farmer is especially attached to giving various boluses to any cow that looks the slightest bit "off."

Environment: Anywhere, anytime.

Physical Exam Findings: Temp of 103.8 F (39.7 C), heart rate increased, lungs clear, rumen slow, no twist (no pings), udder is OK on CMT, uterus is fine, kidney is fine, the left milk vein is blown (abscessed) due to the farmer giving a bottle of dextrose incorrectly (not in the vein but to the side of it). There is a foul odor from the mouth and when feeling the back of the mouth, there is a rip detectable at the top of the throat.

Barn Diagnosis: Pill gun trauma (necrotizing pharyngitis).

Initial Treatment: This is a serious condition needing prompt treatment either with the non-antibiotic treatment of infectious disease (or use antibiotics). I have treated this successfully with: IV 250cc hyper-immune plasma (Plasma Gold or Bovi-Sera), 500cc dextrose with 90cc Phyto-Biotic, 500cc vitamin C.

Follow-up: Feed only very soft feeds (ensiled feeds or fresh pasture). Give oral Phyto-Biotic 20cc twice daily for four days.

Considerations: If no better in 24-36 hours, switch to antibiotics.

PROBLEM: LUMPS & SWELLING

Large Swelling on Jaw

Signalment: Second lactation Holstein, fresh about eight months, confirmed pregnant (about 60 days).

History/Onset: Within last 12 hours.

Environment: Component fed diet, hay, corn silage, grain.

Observable Signs: An obvious swelling on right side of jaw in lower area. Completely off-feed (had been eating normally up until the current morning).

Physical Exam Findings: Temperature 104 F (40 C), heart rate increased, lungs OK, rumen slow, no pings, and lump on right lower jaw is somewhat firm.

Physical Diagnosis: Lumpy Jaw (Actinomycosis).

Initial Treatment: IV sodium iodide (a form of electrolytes), hyperimmune plasma (Plasma Gold or Bovi-Sera) 250cc (to counteract gram negative effects of normally found germs in oral cavity), vitamin C 500cc, Phyto-Biotic tincture 90cc (contains garlic, echinacea, baptisia, hydrastis, barberry) in 500cc dextrose.

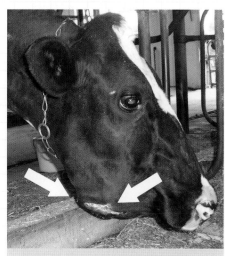

An old case of lumpy jaw with cow able to live normally though the jaw will be permanently enlarged with old scar from drainage at bottom of swelling.

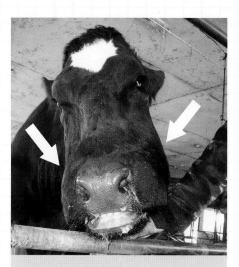

Severe facial swelling that includes areas around muzzle and nose up towards the eyes may indicate an allergic reaction to a spider or snake bite.

Cow with lumpy jaw, just prior to treatment (1).

Same cow as above, four days after initial treatment (2).

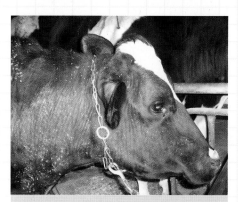

Same cow as above 10 days after initial and follow up treatment at day four. She is eating normally at this point (3).

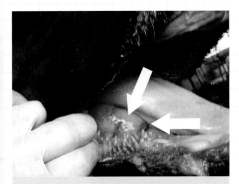

Obvious abscess in jaw of cow. Breath was foul.

Follow-up: Must repeat the IV sodium iodide every four to six days for two times after initial treatment. Give 15cc Phyto-Biotic orally three times daily for four days. Topical peppermint essential oil lotion can be applied to jaw against heat from swelling.

Considerations: The cow has been in milk a long time and is pregnant — should a fever reducer be used to help the cow not get too feverish and possibly abort? Flunixin would be preferred as it is 100 times as strong as aspirin and aspirin has to be given by a pill gun — the cow probably does *not* want things rammed down her mouth, especially with this condition.

Same cow as left, two hours after flunixin was given. Severe swelling has diminished but can still be somewhat seen and evidenced by tongue protruding from mouth.

Note: An animal that has rapidly developed soft swelling (within the last 12 hours) of *both sides* of lower jaw, may have a very serious mouth infection and cellulitis. Cellulitis is an infection of the soft tissues beneath the skin and can rapidly (and fatally) progress, especially if it is happening in the lower mouth region. These are rare, but I have never been able to successfully treat

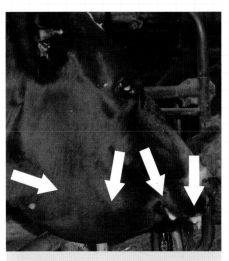

Cow with very significant swelling under both jaws — rapid onset. Likely cellulitis. While Johne's disease can give such a swelling, it is very slow to develop and cows don't tend to salivate (which this one is).

these with natural treatments. It would be a very wise move to use an antibiotic. Doing so will resolve the condition quickly.

Another rather rare condition would be an animal which has an allergic reaction (spider sting, snake bite) that swells the entire face of the cow, creating enormous swelling with impaired circulation, eventually resulting in sloughing of the skin which was stretched too tight. If the case is caught very early, rapid use of dexamethasone, flunixin and antibiotics would be very appropriate.

Older Cow With Some Lumps

Signalment: Eighth lactation Holstein, fresh five months ago.

History/Onset: Farmer noticed the cow is generally slow to eat and walk. Fairly normal but is slowing down, has better days and worse days. No rhyme or reason really. A lump was noticed on her side.

Environment: Anywhere, anytime.

Observable Signs: Lump is obvious on her side.

Physical Exam Findings: A firm lump the size of a fist is located where the prefemoral lymph node is and at the supramammary lymph node as well. On internal examination per rectum, various lumps are easily detected in abdomen.

Barn Diagnosis: Cancer, likely lymphosarcoma.

Initial Treatment: None.

Follow-up: None.

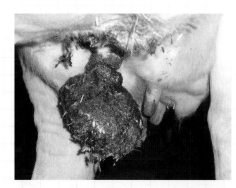

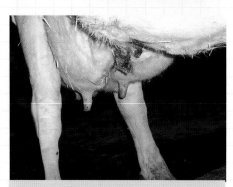

Old cow with cancerous growth hanging from a stalk in the middle of udder for months (left). One day it dropped off (bottom left) — it looks better but it will likely grow back. Cow was fine otherwise.

Considerations: Lymphosarcoma (enzootic bovine leukemia) can be transmitted by blood to other cows. Flies and re-used needles are the most common way. Individual sleeves will help for pregnancy exams *if* flies and needles are *also* being addressed. Sometimes there can be a different cancer that is causing a tumor (though lymphosarcoma is the most common in cattle).

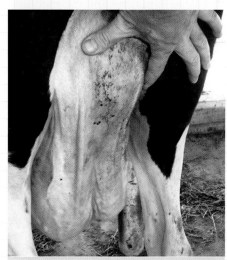

Cow with lumps at lymph nodes in front of leg and at top of udder. These cows will often have internal lumps (tumors).

Has Bumps All Over Her & Off-Feed

Signalment: Older cow fresh about four months, had been milking really well.

History/Onset: Sudden onset between milkings. Farmer saw Jimson weed (*Datura stramonium*) in the hay rack last couple days. However, Jimson weed poisoning should gives hyper-excitability and this cow was very quiet.

Environment: Summertime when lots of different plants are growing and different insects are stinging.

Observable Signs: Many small raised swellings all over trunk, neck, head and legs. Cow is not eating.

Physical Exam Findings: Very slow rumen, no twisted stomach, uterus OK, kidneys OK, udder slack (no milk), ears cool to touch and slightly thickened, eyelids slightly thickened. Cow is dull and listless. Stands up OK but prefers to lie down.

Barn Diagnosis: Allergic reaction (due to unknown substance).

Initial Treatment: As antihistamines have never been added to the National List for organic livestock healthcare, they couldn't be used without removal of the animal from organic production. It was chosen to give her an injection of epinephrine, which can counteract allergic reactions, though different types of reac-

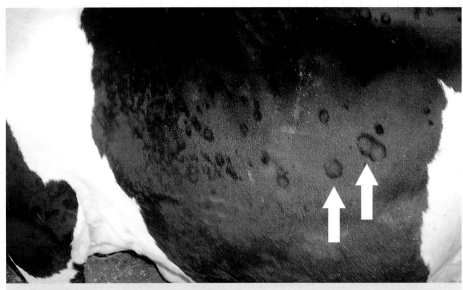

Cow with allergic reaction, most likely a feed (farmer noted Jimpson weed, Datura stramonium, in the baleage).

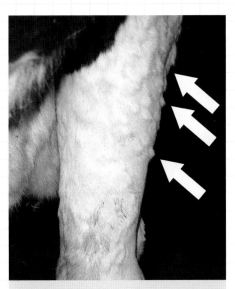

Many raised bumps on leg of same cow.

Cows eyelids were also swollen. Bumps below jaw as well.

tions than what was presented. IV dextrose and CMPK were also given since she was essentially shut down and not taking in any feed, and that she was an older cow and had been milking well. Since it was possibly something she ingested, we pumped her stomach with mineral oil (to coat the gut and not allow reabsorption of toxins) and activated char-

coal (completely vegetable-based source) as well as alfalfa meal.

Follow-up: Give a tube of activated charcoal again in six hours. Give 10 pellets Apis Mel 30C three times that same day as it is truly homeopathic for swellings (especially those where the patient feels better when cool is applied).

Considerations: The next day she was getting back to normal and looked entirely different (no swellings). Try to identify the source of the allergic reation.

PROBLEM: MISCELLANEOUS

Peeling of White Areas of Fur & Some Mastitis

Signalment: Ten-year-old Holstein, just fresh for seventh time.

History/Onset: No problem calving. Came down with milk fever. Responded to IV treatment when farmer administered it.

Environment: Dry cows out on pasture to calve. A recent set of sunny spring days. All kinds of plant growth is happening, both pasture plants and weeds along edges of pasture.

Observable Signs: LH teat watery and quarter is hard (according to farmer). Patches of fur sloughing off.

Physical Exam Findings: Cow is bright and alert, eats a little. Not possible to strip out LH teat due to scab over the end. All four teats have skin peeled off from them and look red. White areas of fur have peeled away, revealing the dermis, which looks irritated, dry and scabby.

Barn Diagnosis: Photosensitization and resulting in sunburn of white areas (most commonly affected as black fur doesn't allow penetration of ultraviolet light).

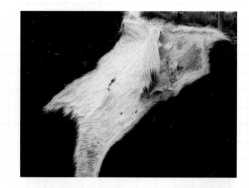

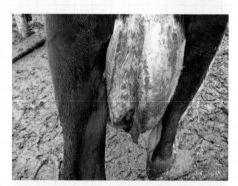

Initial Treatment: For the mastitis give hyperimmune plasma (Plasma Gold or Bovi-Sera), vitamin C, dextrose with herbal antibacterial tincture (90cc Phyto-Biotic) and CMPK.

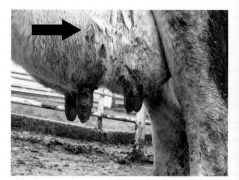

Photosensitization (due to possible liver toxicity). Notice only exposed white and pink areas are affected.

Follow-up: Apply an aloe ointment or gel on all areas that look burned. Allow cow to only be outside at night or on cloudy days for two weeks. Give herbal Celandine, Red Root and Dandelion to help liver.

Considerations: There is a possibility that the cow ate a plant that metabolized to create photosensitization and ended up with sunburn secondarily. However, with toxic plants or any feed intake problem, there are usually at least a few cows affected. In this case of an old cow, there may have been liver impairment to begin with.

PROBLEM: HOT WEATHER

The Weather Has Been Really Hot and a Cow is Weak, Down and/or Panting

Signalment: Usually older cow (but can be any animal), oftentimes recently fresh, especially if there is another problem going on (*i.e.* retained placenta, mastitis, etc.). A dark colored animal is more likely to be affected than a light-colored animal. Might be heavy body weight or very pregnant.

History/Onset: There has been a heat wave happening, this animal seemed a bit weak over the last day and now is down, not wanting to get up when prompted.

Environment: Very high temperatures for the last few days. High humidity makes it worse.

Observable Signs: Cow is weak, down and drowsy. Very warm or hot to touch. Sometimes panting, salivating excessively, holding head over a water source. Off-feed.

Physical Exam Findings: Rectal temperature is high — above 106 F (over 41 C). Pupils dilated, oral and vaginal mucous membranes bright pink and dry. Breathing shallow and increased.

Barn Diagnosis: Heat stroke.

Initial Treatment: Hose down the animal with water for 15-20 minutes. They like this treatment and, if standing, will often stay right there without being held in place. Drench and re-drench *all parts of the body* with some extra focus on the back of the head where the internal thermostat is located. Give IV fluids to re-hydrate (4-5 liters lactated ringers solution, one bottle of dextrose, calcium if recently fresh). Allow animal to drink water as needed or as desired. If not wanting to voluntarily drink, pump stomach with stomach tube to get 5-8 gallons (18.9-30.2 liters) of cool water into the rumen for internal cooling. *Do not* drench by holding the mouth open and pouring water into mouth, they will very likely get it into the lungs. Call a vet for full treatment if not able to do the steps mentioned above. Start hosing the cow prior to vet's arrival. The hosing off with cold water is probably the most important step, but since dehydration goes right along with heat stroke, IV fluids and drinking water are critical as well (pump the stomach if the animal is not starting to drink on its own). Keep in mind that cows can normally drink up to 30 gallons (113 liters) of water *a day* in the summer.

Follow-up: Monitor closely the next day. Hose down again in an hour or two as needed. Giving homeopathic Belladonna hourly for a few hours is definitely good to do (but not as the only treatment!). Keep water in front of animal and available at all times.

Considerations: If the cow is just fresh and down with milk fever (the cause for her not getting out of the sun), treat with IV calcium products *first*. Do not drench a cow in this condition with oral calcium products. After treatment, she will likely raise enough to get her near a water source to start hosing her down.

Animals which have had pneumonia earlier in life will show breathing problems more quickly during summertime than herd mates which have not had pneumonia. These animals have weak lungs due to previous damage from pneumonia. Unfortunately, there is no lasting treatment for such animals.

Heat stroke animals with temperatures up to 108 F (42.2 C) can recover if treated as described. Once an animal temperature is 109 F or above (over 42.7 C), brain damage is likely and even though they may respond to initial treatment, they tend not to fully recover (however, it is still worth the effort to cool them down if it hasn't been going on too long).

PROBLEM: BEHAVIOR ISSUES

Keeps Leaning & Walking to One Side

Signalment: Bred Holstein heifer.

History/Onset: The bred heifers have not been watched as closely since they are in a different barn. The farmer noticed the animal mindlessly circling on its own one morning.

Environment: Any time of year but perhaps more common in late winter or early spring when silage feed may become spoiled.

Observable Signs: There is an obvious, continuous circling of the animal, which will only stop when it runs into a wall and can then lean there for a time. But it will start again fairly soon. If tied in a stall, it will lean dramatically to one side. The same side will show a droopy ear, droopy eye and drooling out of that side of the mouth. The animal won't eat by this time.

Physical Exam Findings: There will be a low-grade fever as well. Tapping the eyebrow doesn't make the animal blink and grabbing the ear is not resisted.

Barn Diagnosis: Listeriosis (circling disease).

Initial Treatment: The infection is that of a germ that has penetrated the brain stem and has affected the cranial nerves at their origin. This will be fatal if not aggressively treated by antibiotics that can penetrate the cerebro-spinal fluid. Usually IV oxytetracycline will be needed, 100cc daily for about four days in a row. Or, give the oxytetracycline at first and follow-up with large doses of penicillin.

Follow-up: As stated above. If pregnant, the animal may abort.

Considerations: Listeriosis is caused by a germ that does best in low oxygen and cold temperature situations. Feeding corn silage which has been moved and then fed out over a number of days in the late winter can be a cause. This is a very difficult disease to treat when the mindless circling is seen. If caught early by the veterinarian when examining the animal and finding the classic cranial nerve paralysis prior to circling, aggressive treatment will be most beneficial. Fortunately this is a rare disease and will usually only affect individual animals.

Bred heifer with head tilt, droopy ear on same side, and drools saliva out of mouth on same side.

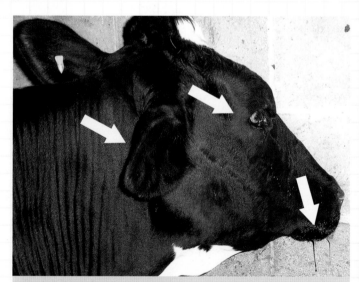

Same animal as left; notice the drooping eye. It's eyebrow muscles are paralyzed and the animal doesn't withdraw when the eyebrow is touched. The eye is open all the time and drying out. Also notice drool and lowered ear on the same side.

Yearling Not Moving Much, Has a Mild Bloat and Its Ears Seem More Perked Up

Signalment: Yearling, but could be any age animal.

History/Onset: The farmer has noticed this one animal not coming up to the feed trough like the rest for the last couple days. She seems to stand on her own and not move as much as the others.

Environment: Large pen with too much rusty hardware protruding from some posts.

Observable Signs: Mild bloat, ears are very erect, the tail is slightly extended (like a pump handle), and the animal almost seems to stand like a "sawhorse."

Physical Exam Findings: No rumen motility, heart rate slightly increased, lungs clear, the tail is indeed slightly extended and won't relax, all four legs seem kind of stiff. When looking into the mouth, it is nearly impossible to open the mouth.

Barn Diagnosis: Lockjaw (tetanus).

Initial Treatment: Tetanus antitoxin and penicillin.

Follow-up: Supportive care: tube feed the animal but perhaps more importantly, relieve the bloat. This is probably best done by placing a temporary rumen trocar into the rumen (where it is bloated). Since tetanus is almost the opposite of botulism, the rumen muscles are "locked," like the jaw. Thus bloat is a very common occurrence with lockjaw. Placing a temporary trocar will also enable feeding the animal to some extent, but more importantly the rumen gases will not buildup.

Considerations: In some full-blown cases (especially in heifers), they are standing so rigidly that pushing on them will tip them over without any resistance on their part. They will go down holding the same rigid leg positions as when they were standing. Like botulism, the initial dose will dictate the course of the disease and its duration. Tetanus toxoid (vaccine) is readily available and used frequently in the equine world but not commonly in the bovine world as bovines are generally more resistant to this disease. It is caused by a puncture, creating a low oxygen environment, which enables the tetanus toxins to rapidly accumulate and spread through the body. If a puncture wound is immediately noticed when it occurs, give homeopathic Ledum, three to four times daily for a few days. Flush the puncture with hydrogen peroxide. If possible, like with a nail in the hoof, open up the area and make sure it bleeds to ensure new, fresh circulation.

PROBLEM: OFF-FEED ISSUES

Weaker Over the Last Few Days, Has Eaten & Drinks Less; She Stands Weakly & There is a Bit of Drool

Signalment: Lactating cow, but not necessarily.

History/Onset: There has been a slow deterioration of the animal over the past couple days. It is getting more and more difficult to get her up. She was treated with IV calcium yesterday, which seemed to help slightly in her getting up.

Environment: The ration consists of wrapped ensiled feed (round bales and a long ag-bag).

Observable Signs: A mild bloat is noticed, no cud chewing, a dazed look to the eyes. Not much manure or urine has been passed in the last day.

Physical Exam Findings: The pupils are dilated, the rumen is not turning over, there is a mild pong at the top of the rumen (gas cap), heart rate is normal, lungs are clear, ears are cool to the touch, udder is normal CMT. The tongue is very slightly visible. *When grab-*

bing the tongue and pulling it out of the mouth, the animal gives no resistance and the tongue hangs out of the mouth momentarily prior to it being slowly drawn back in.

Barn Diagnosis: Botulism.

Initial Treatment: Botulism antitoxin as soon as possible if the animal is still standing. If the animal is down, it is probably too late.

Follow-up: Supportive care: tube feeding the cow since her muscles are paralyzed by weakness due to the botulism toxin present at the nerve-muscle junctions.

Considerations: This condition can happen to a handful of animals at once, though it is usually a single animal disease. Horses are much more sensitive to the botulism toxin than are cows. But the use of wrapped round bales and ag-bags has increased botulism on dairy farms in recent years. The bacteria is in the soil generally (and there can be "hot" botulism micro-regions depending on soils) but only causes its classic damage when the spores are ingested. This is how it can happen: the farmer's hay was rained on twice and then he baled it and wrapped it with the pH being 5 (too high for proper fermentation).

The cow in the photo for this case was one of five animals from a 35-head herd that succumbed to botulism poisoning. Another case was when heifers were eating from the face of an ag-bag during March (below freezing at night and above freezing during the day) while in a

Live cow with botulism: notice tongue hanging loosely out of mouth. This is due to botulism toxin paralyzing muscles, leading to no strength to pull the tongue back in.

low area in the field. Three yearling heifers came down with botulism.

There is a vaccine, which the equine world tends to use since horses are much more sensitive to the effects of the spores. It takes three doses to reach immunity. Like any disease, the amount of initial germ will dictate how severe the signs become. If only a mild dose, the typical signs won't last as long, while a heavy dose will give signs much more quickly and the animal will be down quicker. The problem is that you don't know what the dose was when you are looking at the affected animal(s).

PROBLEM: BEHAVIOR ISSUES

Bred Heifer is Acting Odd & Slobbering

Signalment: Holstein heifer, bred about five months.

History/Onset: The farmer noticed that this heifer is standing on her own away from the other heifers for the past few days. She will come up to the feed bunk later than the others but doesn't really have much interest in eating.

Environment: Late summer, in the pasture area where the growing heifers are kept out back near the woods. There are the usual woodland animals around (raccoons and skunks). One raccoon was seen by the farmer wandering around in the pasture in broad daylight a couple of weeks ago.

Observable Signs: The heifer will occasionally give an odd bellowing noise and look mindlessly into the distance. When approached, she will stand there but react in a spooked way when touched. She generally doesn't move much but occasionally wanders to no particular area. There is a little bit of drool coming from her lower lip most of the time.

Physical Exam Findings: Normal temperature, heart rate normal, lungs normal, eyes seems to be dilated slightly (pupils dilated), ears are normal with both being erect, no bloat or diarrhea, there is no udder swelling. Upon reaching in rectally to check on the pregnancy, she reacts violently.

Barn Diagnosis: Possible rabies (with history of raccoons seen in daytime). A full determination cannot be made unless the animal is sent in for a necropsy (where they will decapitate the head and look at specific areas of the brain).

Initial Treatment: Do not put hands into the mouth of an animal displaying odd behavior, especially if a known rabies carrier species (raccoon, skunk or fox) has been spotted recently during the daytime. Either euthanize with a veterinary euthanasia solution and send in for testing. Never shoot an animal in the head if it will be going for rabies testing.

Follow-up: Monitor closely. If the animal gets better, it cannot be rabies, as rabies *always* gets worse and infected animals will die within 10 days. Also, rabid animals will *not* drink.

Considerations: There are various diseases such as listeriosis, nervous ketosis (in lactating cows), grass tetany and others that affect the brain and behavior of cattle. Rabies can occur in two general forms: furious rabies and "dumb" rabies. Dogs and cats tend to get the furious, violent type of rabies while cattle tend to get the "dumb" type. However, there is definitely no hard and fast rule.

The history of seeing a usually nocturnal species that commonly carries rabies out and about in the daytime is a major tip off. Don't forget that bats also carry rabies and they won't be as easily observed unfortunately.

There is a vaccination available for rabies but it is designed for dogs. However, there may be some equine rabies vaccines available which would be more appropriate for cattle. But remember that vaccination is for prevention, not when the animal has already been exposed. In my thinking, there is no more critical vaccine that has been invented than the rabies vaccine. Rabies is a horrible disease that is preventable by proper vaccination beforehand.

Major Trauma to Nose

Signalment: Black Jersey-Holstein cross, about seven months pregnant.

History/Onset: Instantaneous injury from propeller blades of an un-screened (unprotected) box fan.

Environment: Where cows come into the barn.

Observable Signs: Obvious.

Physical Exam Findings: No time to do. Just get right to the obvious problem.

Barn Diagnosis: Major trauma to the face.

Initial Treatment: Sedate and give analgesia systematically with xylazine and butorphanol and then use lidocaine locally for full local anesthesia. Stitch nose back together.

Follow-up: Anti-inflammatories (flunixin) and calendula ointment.

Considerations: Address the emergency but remember to reverse sedation with tolazine so the calf in the womb is also normalized. Give animal flunixin for a few days to keep swelling to a minimum (to allow healing without the stitches breaking down too early).

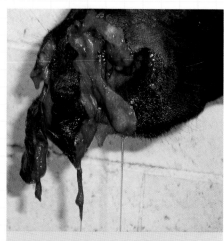

(1) Pregnant heifer that got too curious with an exposed box fan.

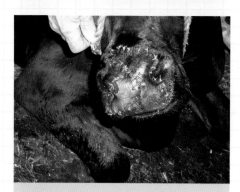

(2) One hour later — about 80 stitches.

(3) Two weeks later, right after stitches were removed.

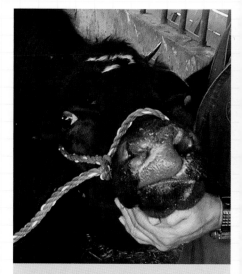

(4) A year and a half later, hardly any evidence except a slight twist to the nose.

GROUP PROBLEMS

Multi-Prong Approach to Prevention & Treatment

Young Stock: Problems caused by parasites such as stomach worms, coccidia, flies and pinkeye should be considered at a herd level. But they still need to include background information, proper diagnosis and holistic approaches to prevention and treatment. Internal parasitism can lead to other problems as the parasite load draws down the immune system's capabilities to withstand other challenges.

Mature Cows: Nutrition is a major factor in dairy cow health. The chart to the right, An Overview of Preventing Common Problems in Dairy Cattle very clearly sums up the cause and effect relationship between diet and some common problems. Understanding this will help a farmer ask better questions of his/her farm advisors if there are problems.

Post-Weaning Parasitism: A Weak Link

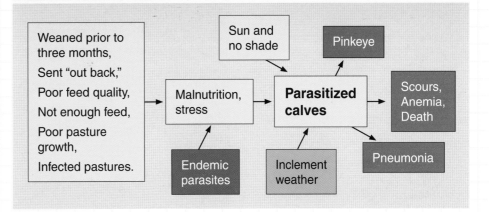

AN OVERVIEW OF PREVENTING COMMON PROBLEMS IN DAIRY CATTLE

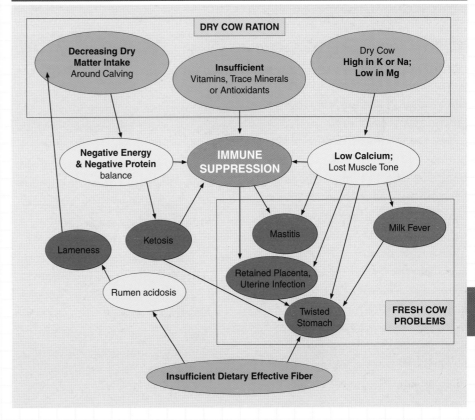

Chart: An overview of preventing commmon problems in dairy cattle. Adapted from J.P. Goff, *Journal of Dairy Science,* 2006.

Internal Parasites

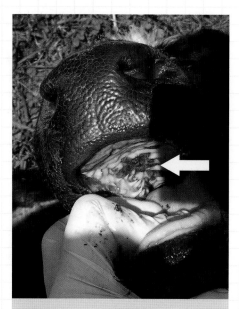

Notice the ulcerated areas on the roof of the mouth. This is from a calf that was barely alive and infested with stomach worms.

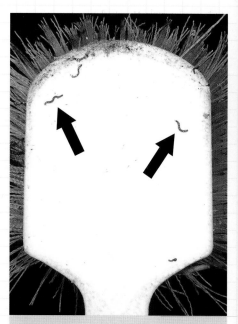

The farmer noticed small red squirming things when he cleaned out the water trough in the weaned calf pasture. Upon inspection under a microscope, these were found to be adult stomach worms. They are red from sucking the blood of the calves. I had never seen free living stomach worms, only the eggs.

Oftentimes farmers ask me what wormers are available for use that are approved for organics. This thinking is understandable since such thinking has been constantly drummed up on the conventional side of things. However, this is pure "input-substitution" type thinking (*i.e.* which silver bullet will be available when I need to treat?). Unfortunately the reliance on silver bullets in the wormer industry has led to resistance developing to ivermectin throughout the world. Instead, we really need to think about the entire life cycle of the stomach worm, both inside *and* outside of the animal. Veterinarians need to start doing this as well.

Yes, the worms reproduce in the animal but they also live outside on the pasture, waiting to be taken in again with every blade of grass to re-start their life cycle within the animal. We should think about appropriate *pasture management* to reduce the livability of the free living worm larvae. This would basically include anything that will dry out their environment. In southern areas, paddocks become essentially sterilized of worms during the hottest months. The larvae simply dry

up and die and are not able to re-infect animals when they come back onto the pasture. In more northern areas with less prolonged intense heat, breaking up the manure paddies is most important, since it is these paddies which harbor the newest eggs and which are ready to hatch out larvae. Therefore, clipping pastures, or at least dragging them, will likely yield excellent results with dramatically lowered larvae counts. Clipping pastures also gives the advantage of uniform re-growth and cutting down unwanted plant species that may go to seed.

However, if you are opposed to mechanically managing paddocks, have chickens and/or hogs follow

groups of animals through the paddocks. There will be less stomach worm larvae and fly larva/maggots. Why? Because chickens love to peck at the manure paddies and hogs love to root through manure paddies, destroying the paddies and thereby eliminating stomach worm larvae and fly hatching areas. To reduce flies from hatching on manure paddies, place chickens into paddocks *two days after the cows have grazed* as this will optimize the time for fly larva to be eaten when chickens peck the manure paddies apart.

By feeding animals the soil fungus *Dudingtonia flagrans,* free living nematodes in the soil are reduced due to the strangulating effect of this type of fungus upon the free living nematodes.

By inter-planting the pastures with certain species like chicory and birdsfoot trefoil that are high in tannins, worm loads have been shown to be reduced compared to feeding only a standard pasture composition of rye and white clover. In arid areas, consider planting sainfoin (a legume which does not cause bloat). Various plant species contain tannins; these phytochemicals can enhance the animal's gut or make the gut less hospitable to worms. Additionally, there are certain plant medicines that exert parasitical effects when given orally to animals in their feed or as boluses.

In short, taking all these preventive approaches will create a much more balanced life for the animals at risk of worm infection without relying on a wormer like ivermectin that has unfortunately created resistance due to its initial "magical" silver bullet qualities.

Coccidia infection generally occurs in young dairy animals that are housed in the same surroundings where other groups of young animals previously have been continuously housed. The best way to prevent coccidia infection is to use hutches or

Moribund (near dead) calf due to extreme internal parasitism treated ineffectively (walnut hulls only). Notice the fluid under the jaw — this is due to excessive protein loss. This case is an example of either complete gullibility by farmer that natural treatments are always better or simple abject neglect. Either is unacceptable for animal welfare and actually illegal according to USDA National Organic Program law.

super hutches (group housing) which are movable to different areas. It is almost that simple.

The worst situations, in my experience, are nearly weaned calves that are in the same box stall, or group pen, year after year, especially areas with dirt floors that allow the coccidia to "hide" and wait until a new group arrives. These kinds of areas need rest time between groups, which usually isn't done. However, fresh air, sunshine, disinfectant, and dry conditions can go a long way. Still, portable housing is much better. Feeding whole milk instead of milk replacer will nearly always provide a stronger calf and

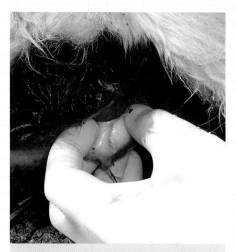

Inspecting the mucous membranes of the vulva of the calf at left shows very pale coloration (compare to white exam gloves). Extreme anemia (low red blood cell count due to internal parasitism).

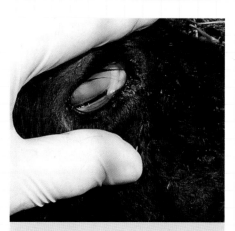

Another way to assess mucous membrane color is by looking at the eye socket and the third eyelid. Again, nearly as white as the exam gloves.

a healthier gut, making it more difficult for coccidia to cause a problem.

Calves Have Poor Hair Coat, Diarrhea & a Slight Cough

Signalment: Six- to nine-month-old calves (Holsteins, Jerseys and Holstein-Jersey mixes).

History/Onset: Calves were born in March, April and May and were abruptly weaned at approximately 3 months of age. They were then put on the usual paddock in June, July and August, where calves are always placed at that age. Now it is beginning of autumn and the animals are being brought back inside for the winter months.

Environment: Paddock has had some pasture grass but also has had weeds and bare dirt. There has been a damp and cool spell lately.

Observable Signs: Runny manure and frank diarrhea. Hair coats are rough; some black animals have a slight reddish tint. Bellies look round and slightly enlarged and can see the ribs easily. Some animals have a short, dry hacking cough when moved around. All are eating fairly well.

Physical Exam Findings: Pale pink to very pale mucous membranes, increased heart rate (even after calming down after catching), some animals have a white discharge from the nostrils and raspy lung sounds. These animals have a low-grade fever. This is a situation where there are two problems happening at the same time.

Barn Diagnosis: Parasitism due to internal worm infestation with an opportunistic secondary pneumonia starting.

Initial Treatment: Get the animals outside into fresh air immediately. Do not keep them confined in an enclosed area, as the coughing will likely get worse. Use Immunoboost, 1cc per 200 lbs. under the skin or in the muscle.

Use a s proven commercial, effective wormer to kill the massive numbers of internal parasites that are drawing down the animals' immune systems and making them anemic as well — this would include ivermectin, moxidectin or fenbendazole. Check with your certifier about which is allowable since the USDA National Organic Standards Board (NOSB) has recommended that fenbendazole replace ivermectin. Any treatment should be used immediately, one time. No need to repeat unless *really* needed.

Just get the animals re-set, and then use natural treatments to keep things in balance. An ideal product is called Ferro, since it causes constipation and builds iron and has numerous minerals to help build the animals back up.

Follow-up: Close monitoring. Any calves that worsen with coughing should have veterinary attention. There may be need to treat one or two animals in a group of 10-15

Terrible damp environment for calves. One spell of rainy, cold weather will send these calves into a respiratory condition.

with an antibiotic if they are too far into the pneumonia process. The rest will probably get better with the advice given above *if* there is increased care, time and attention

given to this group of animals for a few weeks. Do not rely on helpers to tell you how they are doing — you must inspect them yourself. Gathering some manure samples and having a fecal flotation done will likely show some animals to be heavily infested with strongyle worms while some are only moderately so and some will be lighted infected. The lightest infestations will probably be the best looking animals while the heaviest infestations will likely be the ones that look the worst and are coughing.

Considerations: Spring calves that are weaned and then put onto the usual "weaned calf" pasture are highly likely to become parasitized since the usual stomach worm egg larva hatch and move to the tips of the grass to be eaten and repeat their life cycle. Stomach worms reach peak populations on pasture in July, August and September. Pasture management is critical. Clipping to drag the manure paddies

apart and dry out the larva, having chicken to peck the manure paddies apart, etc. is critical.

Note: A few calves may become fatally infested with stomach worms. This usually occurs when the farmer is relying upon a natural product alone and not doing any pasture management at all. It is truly a pity and a total breach of animal welfare if this situation arises since the animal is too far gone to help it, when it could have easily been treated had it been taken care of properly.

By the way, Pinkeye is commonly seen in these calves as well. This is usually due to rank growth that they poke their eyes through to get at any lush pasture that may be there. The irritation of the rank growth makes their eyes water and flies are attracted to the moisture, possibly delivering the bacteria *Moraxella bovis* to the calf's eye and starting the infection. Strongly consider using a pinkeye vaccine for weaned calves put to pasture.

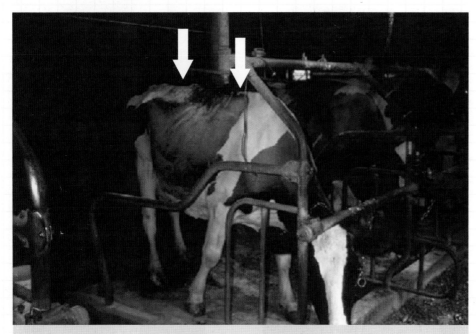

Field lime (calcium carbonate) heavily applied to the animal can keep the animal drier and not attract flies. Apply as often as needed.

Fly trap box with a pheromone attractant underneath the dome-shaped screen.

Flies

Fly control truly exemplifies the multi-prong, holistic approach. The main goal of fly prevention and control is to realize that flies, like most parasites, rely on moist surroundings to reproduce. It is critically important to *not* have a build up of manure (fresh and aging), as flies absolutely love these kinds of areas. But more importantly is that anything that will make the environment or the animals drier will reduce flies.

In my experience, tunnel ventilation is the absolute most effective way to reduce fly problems in barns. Flies simply cannot fight the air current created by tunnel ventilation. The only draw back is that grazing cattle won't be spending much time in the barn. However, on the hottest days when cows don't want to be outside anyway, it probably is best to have the cows out for a few hours in the morning and bring them back in by late morning when it's starting to get real hot. Then let them out again for the evening after milking time.

Other barn control for flies includes using strategically placed predator wasps that eat fly larvae (maggots), sticky tape stretched in various areas and fly traps with pheromones that attract flies to an entrapment area.

A very interesting device is a powerful "fly vacuum" cleaner chamber. This device is placed at a common entry/exit area, and as the cows walk through it, a strong force of air is aimed at the cow from one side and then on the other side is a strong vacuum of air to suck flies into a large holding tank (which is emptied as needed). This device has great potential and hopefully it becomes fully marketed.

As for the animals themselves, applying lime powder to the backs of the animals to prevent their fur from glistening with moisture can go a long way. This is cheap and it is OK to be liberal with it, as it will fall off cows as they are outside on pasture and fertilize the ground.

Last to be employed (after other measures are in place) is the use of a variety of botanical fly sprays that are commercially available for organics. It is interesting how many transitioning organic farmers always ask right away what fly spray they can use once they are organic. If farmers simply want to practice "input substitution" by switching from one chemical fly spray to a

Two walk through boxes with screening and pheromones to brush off flies, attract them to the screens, and then trap them.

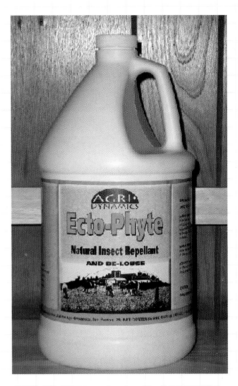

Barrel Feeder with solar-powered sprayer. Great for outside heifers.

gentler botanical fly spray, they will be sorely disappointed *unless* they also realize that a multi-prong approach is truly needed for fly prevention and control.

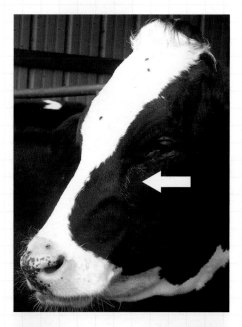

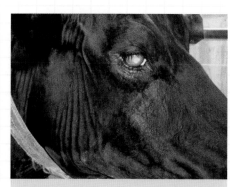

Pinkeye once the intense pain has subsided. The time between symptoms shown in photos (left and above) is usually when the animal will be squinting from the intense pain from the pinkeye infection.

Pinkeye

Prevention: Since pinkeye is very dependent on flies to transmit the causative bacteria, *Moraxella bovis*, it is no surprise that fly reduction is critical in preventing pinkeye. However, by considering also that flies are attracted to moisture, it is actually still very important to *clip pastures*. Why? Clipping pastures is important because there won't be brittle, rank growth that animals will have to nose their way through to get to the more lush undergrowth. The rank growth can poke and irritate their eyes, which will begin to water. The slight bit of moist drainage from the eye which may be observed on some animals' faces during the summer season is almost a sure of sign that pinkeye is starting. If you look closely enough there will oftentimes be flies sitting on the drainage.

As with general fly control, good ventilation goes a long way to reducing fly pressures and associated pinkeye. Since vaccines are allowed by organic rules, it would be advisable to vaccinate animals, *especially weanlings put out to pasture.*

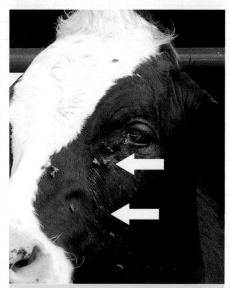

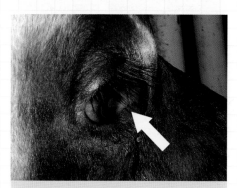

Pinkeye — notice the raised red area in the center of the eye. This area as ulcerated and allowed a portion of the more internal part of the eye to come forth. Notice wet drainage.

Two views of same animal: eye is "sleepy" with moist drainage coming out. Notice flies on the drainage. This is typical of pinkeye at its earliest stage. Notice flies near drainage. Whether the flies created the irritation and now eye has excess drainage or if the animal accidentally poked her eye on rank vegetative growth, the flies are the known carrier of the pinkeye germ Moraxella bovis.

There is an easy one shot, under the skin vaccine available (Maxi/Guard, Piliguard). However, there are unfortunately different strains of pinkeye (cow and sheep variants) and the vaccines don't cover them all.

Treatment: For any animals with pinkeye it is very important to *keep them out of direct sunlight* as the ultraviolet rays make the condition worse. Keep affected animals away from the sun during the day but let them out at night. Alternatively, because many graziers will not keep animals off pasture during season, using an eye patch on affected animals would be beneficial.

Additionally, the vaccine can be helpful to stop an infection but only *if given very early*. Once the infection is fully established, the conventional treatment is to use antibiotics on the eye, either as a spray, infusion or an injection (injection only to be done by veterinarian). On organic farms, I will use a biologic compound (Plasma Gold) and inject actual antibodies under the first layer of the cornea. This appears to work better on calves than on cows. While this specific treatment will not necessarily clear up an infection quickly, it does stop its advance and allows resolution to begin. Another way is to simply spritz the eye with the Plasma Gold or Bovi-Sera twice daily for a few days.

Surgical closure of the third eyelid across the eye is also an option, only to be done by a veterinarian. This is no more involved than an eyeball injection and should be considered depending on how the follow-up will be. If no follow-up is possible, the surgical closure or the eyeball injection makes sense.

Afterwards the animal can go outside with the group. A labor intensive but gentle treatment is to spray the eye with calendula (water-based or *highly* diluted alcohol-based) four times daily. Keep the cow inside during the day and let out at night.

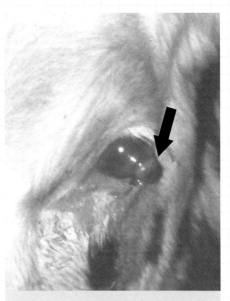

Permanent damage from pinkeye; eyeball contents burst forth a long time ago; this is what remains (no vision).

Weaned Heifers Have Dry, Gray Patches on Head & Neck

Signalment: Animals between the ages of 6-15 months of age.

History/Onset: Little by little over the last few months these heifers started to show gray patches that have gotten bigger.

Environment: Wintertime; stalls which have been used repeatedly over the years and are most likely made of wood to some degree.

Observable Signs: Gray, scaly areas without hair are seen on the nose, around the eyes, and at the neck.

Physical Exam Findings: Nothing remarkable aside from the obvious lesions.

Typical areas of ringworm.

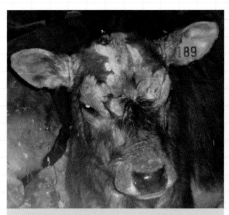

Severe ringworm, the blue is from the farmer's futile use of copper sulphate powder.

Barn Diagnosis: Ringworm (it's actually a fungus).

Initial Treatment: Ringworm generally fades away once the heifers are put out to pasture. There can be an association with a lack of sunlight, lack of vitamin A, and the wood holding the fungus over the years.

However, if needed, the areas can be scrubbed with Betadine. However, wear gloves, as the condition is contagious to humans as well. Some advocate using homeopathic Bacilinum 200C one time. Ringworm tends to disappear on an animal after about 28 days since the fungus is living on the outermost layer of skin, which will naturally shed little by little anyway.

Follow-up: Change out the wood for a metal surface to prevent future problems.

Considerations: If ringworm is found in mature cows, I find this to be concerning as it most likely has to do with a compromised immune system.

GROUP PROBLEMS

Heifers Have Warts

Signalment: Usually bred heifers.

History/Onset: Usually begins with one animal and spreads rapidly.

Environment: Most likely indoors.

Observable Signs: Various sizes of "cauliflower" growths all over the body in several areas.

Physical Exam Findings: Nothing remarkable other than the obvious growths.

Barn Diagnosis: Papillomavirus induced warts.

Initial Treatment: By pulling one off from the animal, this will alert the animal's immune system to fight off the condition. If pulling off really large ones, a vessel which is feeding the wart may spurt, and will need to be clamped off or stitched shut.

Follow-up: Homeopathic thuja 30C, twice daily for five to seven days.

Considerations: This can be a major problem if the wart is near the teat end. The homeopathic treatment (Thuja 30C) has worked in those instances. If the warts are flat (as opposed to cauliflower-like), try homeopathic Sabina 30C twice daily for five to seven days. There are vaccines available (made from warts). They are not very effective once the condition is present. This condition may be seen only one time in a group of animals and not at other times with different animals of the same age group.

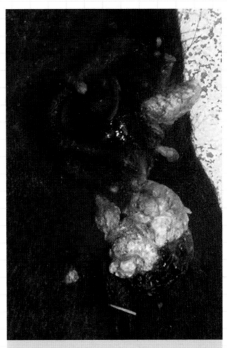

Warts near eye of bull.

GROUP PROBLEMS

Herd Has High Somatic Cell Count (SCC), Not Due To Contagious Strep Ag or Staph Aureus

Signalment: Lactating cows.

History/Onset: The bulk tank somatic cell count has been increasing over the past four months. The farmer switched teat dips in an effort to stop the problem. No results so far. The milk company and vet ran milk culture samples and they came back positive for environmental strep and environmental staph, along with a few coliforms. The milking system technician came in the other day and found the system to be in good working order.

Environment: Any season, but perhaps when more time is spent with the cows (not the growing season).

Observable Signs: None, except that the milk company inspector keeps showing up.

Physical Exam Findings: When feeling the udders for any irregularities and then examining the teats carefully, teat end rings were observed on all four teats on many cows.

Barn Diagnosis: Teat end hyperkeratosis. Over-milking (keeping the machines on too long) or excessive vacuum fluctuation at the teat ends leading to proplapsed (drawn outwardly) teat sphincters, which are seen as teat end rings. These teat end rings will gather dirt, which then enters the teat canal and eventually the udder to cause a reaction (high SCC).

Initial Treatment: Make sure that all cows are prepped correctly and the machines are placed onto the teats within 30-60 seconds from prep in order to take full advantage of the natural oxytocin let down. About 95 percent of all cows will be finished milking in three to five minutes. Machines that are on for longer than this in general can cause teat end rings. There also can be teat end prolapsing (as seen by teat end rings) if there is greater then 2mm vacuum fluctuation change at the teat end during milking time (*not* only during the middle of the day when the technician is checking the vacuum line when no cows are being milked). Correct these problems if present!

Follow-up: Unfortunately, teat end damage can happen very quickly but can take a few months to heal up.

Considerations: Make sure that proper milking technique is being done for every milking on every cow. Having different people milking is one of the easiest ways for high somatic cell counts to spike.

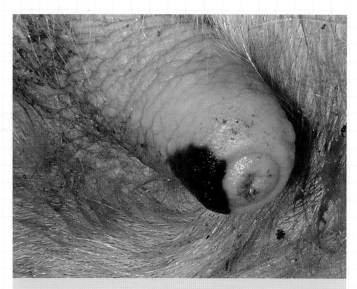

Teat end ring — indicates fluctuating vacuum during milking (or over milking, if only one teat).

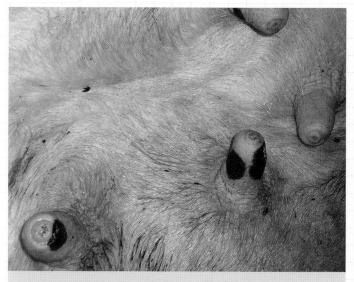

All 4 teat ends are prolapsed, indicating fluctuating vacuum levels during milking times

GROUP PROBLEMS

Several Cows Are Off-Feed & Have Diarrhea

Signalment: Cows in various parts of lactation are sick. They are off-feed and they have had diarrhea. Some bred heifers and yearlings housed in an adjacent barn are also showing some of the same signs.

History/Onset: A group of heifers were recently brought back from a heifer grower in another part of the county. At the heifer grower's place, animals from a few different farms are raised together.

Environment: Tie-stall barn for the milking cows and a free stall/loafing area barn for the younger stock and dry cows. It is October and the animals have all been brought back inside since the grazing season is winding down and the weather has been damp and chilly.

Observable Signs: Fifteen of 60 cows are off-feed (not eating). Some are grinding their teeth. Some have had watery blood-tinged diarrhea. Others have slight diarrhea while others have normal manure.

Physical Exam Findings: Temperatures are normal. Heart rate is slightly elevated. Lungs are non-remarkable. Rumen is slow. There is diarrhea heard on the lower right abdomen when balloted. Grinding of teeth is evident. Many cows are pregnant at various stages. Oral ulcers were found on two younger animals that were examined in the large free stall area.

Barn Diagnosis: Likely BVD (bovine viral diarrhea), classical outbreak.

Initial Treatment: Immune stimulation (since it is a virus). Immuno-boost 1cc/200 lbs. under the skin, in the muscle or in the vein. Intra-nasal modified live vaccine (TSV-2, Nasalgen, Onset). Phyto-Biotic (has ginseng in it, a proven botanically based immune stimulant), 15cc three times daily. Vitamin C IV or IM as a strong antioxidant. Possibly also use a hyperimmune plasma that has specific antibodies to BVD.

Follow-up: Homeopathic Merc Corr 30C three to four times daily — very indicated due to the mucosal ulcerations of mouth, esophagus and rest of digestive tract.

Considerations: If BVD is diagnosed, animals exposed to the situation which are 50-120 days pregnant will likely give birth to persistently infected (PI) BVD calves, if the calves aren't aborted during the crisis. PI calves may be born weak and die, may grow poorly and be culled, or may not show any abnormalities and enter the milking string two years later. However, every moment they are alive, they are shedding millions of live BVD virus into their environment. *No vaccine will overcome the presence of even one PI BVD animal in the herd.* These animals must be identified and removed from the herd immediately (even if they are milking 100 lbs. of milk when identified). Herds that have PI animals in them tend to continually have odd problems occurring, such as lingering reproductive problems and respiratory problems without any obvious causes. The ear notch method for detection/diagnosis of a PI animal is the best method. All animals in a herd need to be done if BVD is truly to be eliminated.

NATIONAL ORGANIC PROGRAM RULE (7 CFR 205.603-205.604)
National List of Allowed Synthetic Substances for Organic Livestock

NOP STANDARD RULE

§ 205.603 SYNTHETIC SUBSTANCES ALLOWED FOR USE IN ORGANIC LIVESTOCK PRODUCTION

In accordance with restrictions specified in this section the following synthetic substances may be used in organic livestock production:

(a) As disinfectants, sanitizer, and medical treatments as applicable.

(1) Alcohols.

(i) Ethanol-disinfectant and sanitizer only, prohibited as a feed additive.

(ii) Isopropanol-disinfectant only.

(2) Aspirin-approved for health care use to reduce inflammation.

(3) Atropine (CAS -51-55-8) — federal law restricts this drug to use by or on the lawful written or oral order of a licensed veterinarian, in full compliance with the AMDUCA and 21 CFR part 530 of the Food and Drug Administration regulations. Also, for use under 7 CFR Part 205, the NOP requires:

(i) Use by or on the lawful written order of a licensed veterinarian; and

(ii) A meat withdrawal period of at least 56 days after administering to livestock intended for slaughter; and a milk discard period of at least 12 days after administering to dairy animals.

(4) Biologics — Vaccines.

(5) Butorphanol (CAS -42408-82-2) — federal law restricts this drug to use by or on the lawful written or oral order of a licensed veterinarian, in full compliance with the AMDUCA and 21 CFR part 530 of the Food and Drug Administration regulations. Also, for use under 7 CFR Part 205, the NOP requires:

(i) Use by or on the lawful written order of a licensed veterinarian; and

(ii) A meat withdrawal period of at least 42 days after administering to livestock intended for slaughter; and a milk discard period of at least 8 days after administering to dairy animals.

(6) Chlorhexidine — Allowed for surgical procedures conducted by a veterinarian. Allowed for use as a teat dip when alternative germicidal agents and/or physical barriers have lost their effectiveness.

(7) Chlorine materials — disinfecting and sanitizing facilities and equipment. Residual chlorine levels in the water shall not exceed the maximum residual disinfectant limit under the Safe Drinking Water Act.

(i) Calcium hypochlorite.

(ii) Chlorine dioxide.

(iii) Sodium hypochlorite.

(8) Electrolytes — without antibiotics.

(9) Flunixin (CAS -38677-85-9) — in accordance with approved labeling; except that for use under 7 CFR Part 205, the NOP requires a withdrawal period of at least two-times that required by the FDA.

(10) Furosemide (CAS -54-31-9) — in accordance with approved labeling; except that for use under 7 CFR Part 205, the NOP requires a withdrawal period of at least two-times that required that required by the FDA.

(11) Glucose.

(12) Glycerine — Allowed as a livestock teat dip, must be produced through the hydrolysis of fats or oils.

(13) Hydrogen peroxide.

(14) Iodine.

(15) Magnesium hydroxide (CAS -1309-42-8) — federal law restricts this drug to use by or on the lawful written or oral order of a licensed veterinarian, in full compliance with the AMDUCA and 21 CFR part 530 of the Food and Drug Administration regulations. Also, for use under 7 CFR part 205, the NOP requires use by or on the lawful written order of a licensed veterinarian.

(16) Magnesium sulfate.

(17) Oxytocin — use in postparturition therapeutic applications.

(18) Paraciticides. Ivermectin — prohibited in slaughter stock, allowed in emergency treatment for dairy and breeder stock when organic system plan-approved preventive management does not prevent infestation. Milk or milk products from a treated animal cannot be labeled as provided for in subpart D of this part for 90 days following treatment. In breeder stock, treatment cannot occur during the last third of gestation if the progeny will be sold as organic and must not be used during the lactation period for breeding stock.

(19) Peroxyacetic/peracetic acid (CAS -79-21-0) — for sanitizing facility and processing equipment.

(20) Phosphoric acid — allowed as an equipment cleaner, Provided, That, no direct contact with organically managed livestock or land occurs.

(21) Poloxalene (CAS -9003-11-6) — for use under 7 CFR Part 205, the NOP requires that poloxalene only be used for the emergency treatment of bloat.

(22) Tolazoline (CAS -59-98-3) — federal law restricts this drug to use by or on the lawful written or oral order of a licensed veterinarian, in full compliance with the AMDUCA and 21 CFR part 530 of the Food and Drug Administration regulations. Also, for use under 7 CFR Part 205, the NOP requires:

(i) Use by or on the lawful written order of a licensed veterinarian;

(ii) Use only to reverse the effects of sedation and analgesia caused by Xylazine; and

(iii) A meat withdrawal period of at least 8 days after administering to livestock intended for slaughter; and a milk discard period of at least 4 days after administering to dairy animals.

(23) Xylazine (CAS -7361-61-7) — federal law restricts this drug to use by or on the lawful written or oral order of a licensed veterinarian, in full compliance with the AMDUCA and 21 CFR part 530 of the Food and Drug Administration regulations. Also, for use under 7 CFR Part 205, the NOP requires:

(i) Use by or on the lawful written order of a licensed veterinarian;

(ii) The existence of an emergency; and

(iii) A meat withdrawal period of at least 8 days after administering to livestock intended for slaughter; and a milk discard period of at least 4 days after administering to dairy animals.

(b) As topical treatment, external parasiticide or local anesthetic as applicable.

(1) Copper sulfate.

(2) Iodine.

(3) Lidocaine — as a local anesthetic. Use requires a withdrawal period of 90 days after administering to livestock intended for slaughter and 7 days after administering to dairy animals.

(4) Lime, hydrated — as an external pest control, not permitted to cauterize physical alterations or deodorize animal wastes.

(5) Mineral oil — for topical use and as a lubricant.

(6) Procaine — as a local anesthetic, use requires a withdrawal period of 90 days after administering to livestock intended for slaughter and 7 days after administering to dairy animals.

(7) Sucrose octanoate esters (CAS s-42922-74-7; 58064-47-4) — in accordance with approved labeling.

(c) As feed supplements — None.

(d) As feed additives.

(1) DL-Methionine, DL-Methionine — hydroxy analog, and DL-Methionine — hydroxy analog calcium (CAS -59-51-8; 63-68-3; 348-67-4) — for use only in organic poultry production until October 1, 2008.

(2) Trace minerals, used for enrichment or fortification when FDA approved.

(3) Vitamins, used for enrichment or fortification when FDA approved.

(e) As synthetic inert ingredients as classified by the Environmental Protection Agency (EPA), for use with nonsynthetic substances or synthetic substances listed in this section and used as an active pesticide ingredient in accordance with any limitations on the use of such substances.

(1) EPA List 4 — Inerts of Minimal Concern.

(2) [Reserved]

(f) Excipients, only for use in the manufacture of drugs used to treat organic livestock when the excipient is: Identified by the FDA as Generally Recognized As Safe; Approved by the FDA as a food additive; or Included in the FDA review and approval of a New Animal Drug Application or New Drug Application.

NOP STANDARD RULE

§205.604 Nonsynthetic Substances Prohibited for Use in Organic Livestock Production

The following nonsynthetic substances may not be used in organic livestock production:

(a) Strychnine.

Sources of Trade Names Mentioned in the Medicine Cabinet

Phyto-Mast, Plasma Gold, Phyto-Biotic, Heat Seek, Get Well, Phyto-Gest, Ferro

Dr. Hubert Karreman
Penn Dutch Cow Care
555 Red Hill Road
Narvon, Pennsylvania 17555
Phone: 717-768-7088
E-mail: penndutch@earthlink.net
Website: www.penndutchcowcare.org
10 years of free monthly newsletters online.

Biocel CBT, Ecto-Phyte

Agri-Dynamics
P.O. Box 267
6574 South Delaware Drive
Martins Creek, Pennsylvania 18063
Phone: 610-250-9280
or 877-393-4484
E-mail: info@agri-dynamics.com
Website: www.agri-dynamics.com

Immunoboost

Bioniche Animal Health
1551 Jennings Mill Road,
Suite 3200A
Bogart, Georgia 30622
Phone: 706-549-4503
or 888-549-4503
Fax: (706) 548-0659
Website: www.bionicheanimalhealth.com

RumenAider, Pyck-Me-Up (Organic), Generator Elite (Organic), Pecti-Cap (Organic), Cal-D Cap (Organic)

Bio-Vet
P.O. Box 115
Blue Mounds, Wisconsin 53517
Phone: 800-246-8381
or 608-437-8891
Fax: 608-437-8883
E-mail: bio-vet@bio-vet.com
Website: www.bio-vet.com

Bovi-Sera

Colorado Serum Company
P.O. Box 16428
4950 York Street
Denver, Colorado 80216-0428
Phone: 800-525-2065
Fax: 303-295-1923
E-mail: colorado-serum@colorado-serum.com

Utresept

Integrated Bio Systems
34282 Manufacturers Way
Abbotsford, British Columbia
V2S 7M1 Canada
Phone: 877-501-5003
Fax: 604-852-9016
E-mail: intbiosys@shaw.ca
Website: www.integratedbiosys.com

Royal Uterine Capsules

Van Beek Natural Science
3689 460th Street
Orange City, Iowa 51041
Phone: 712-737-2958
or 800-346-5311
Fax: 712-737-2878
E-mail: info@vanbeeknatural-science.com
Website: www.vanbeeknatural-science.com

HOMEOPATHIC REMEDIES

Common remedies to stock in the medicine cabinet: **Aconite, Apis, Antimonium, Arnica, Arsenicum, Belladonna, Bryonia, Calc Carb, Cal-Phos, Carbo Veg, Caulophyllum, Hepar Sulph, Hypericum, Iodium, Lycopodium, Merc Corr, Nux Vomica, Phos, Phytolacca, Pulsatilla, Pyrogen, SSC (Sulfur-Silica-Carbo Veg), Sepia, Sabina, Silica, Sulfur, Ustilago**

Homeopathic Laboratories
Jack Borneman, RPh.
1006 West 8th Avenue
King of Prussia, Pennsylvania 19406

Phone: 800-234-8879
Fax Orders: 610-337-2703
Fax Prescriptions: 800-296-8998
E-mail: info@homeopathiclaboratories.com
Website: www.txoptions.com

This homeopathic pharmacy is very professional with excellent service and prompt delivery of orders.

Stomach pump, stethoscope, magnets, IV line, electric prod, ketone strips, calving chains, calf tube feeder, butane powered dehorner (Portosol), infusion pipettes, teat dilators, pill gun, syringes, needles.

Injectible vitamin A, D & E; B-complex; vitamin B$_{12}$ (low potency); vaccines, calcium gel tubes; pink laxative pills, mineral oil; alcohol and alcohol prep pads; 23% calcium, dextrose, hypertonic saline; poloxalene (for pasture bloat); activated charcoal.

Any good farm supply store (generally those in strong dairy areas will have the items listed) or www.enasco.com.

MuSe, Poly Serum, Bovi-Sera, Vaccines, Betadine (surgical iodine scrub), iodine antiseptic pills, vitamin B$_{12}$ (high potency), vitamin C, vitamin K, epinephrine, CMPK, Cal-Phos #2, Lactated ringers solution, Sodium iodide, Thera-Bloat (poloxalene for pasture bloat)

Stomach pump, stethoscope, magnets, IV line, electric prod, ketone strips, calving chains, calf tube feeder, butane powered dehorner (Portasol), infusion pipettes, teat dilators, pill gun, syringes, needles

Injectible Vitamin A, D & E; vitamin B-complex; calcium gel tubes; pink laxative pills, mineral oil; alcohol and alcohol prep pads; 23% calcium, dextrose, hypertonic saline; activated charcoal

Contact your local veterinarian who has a valid client patient relationship (VCPR) with you and your herd of animals. Dr. Karreman is always available to help your local veterinarian with questions about organics.

Allowable Rx Materials on 7CFR205.603 (flunixin, butorphanol, xylazine, tolazoline)

Contact your local veterinarian who has a valid client patient relationship (VCPR) with you and your herd of animals. Dr. Karreman is always available to help your local veterinarian with questions about organics.

Also by Hubert J. Karreman, V.M.D.

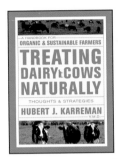

Treating Dairy Cows Naturally
Thoughts & Strategies

By Hubert J. Karreman, V.M.D.

A dairy practitioner describes how cows can be treated for a wide variety of problems with plant-derived and biological medicines. Drawing upon veterinary treatments from the days before synthetic pharmaceuticals and tempering them with modern knowledge and clinical experience, Dr. Karreman bridges the world of natural treatments with life in the barn in a rational and easy to understand way. In describing treatments for common dairy cow diseases, he covers practical aspects of biologics, botanical medicines, homeopathic remedies, acupuncture and conventional medicine. This book will serve as a useful reference for years to come. *Hardcover, 420 pages. ISBN 978-1-601730-00-8*

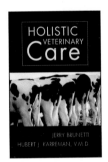

Veterinary Care

By Jerry Brunetti & Hubert J. Karreman, V.M.D.

Dr. Hubert J. Karreman, author of the compendium *Treating Dairy Cows Naturally,* is joined by renowned animal nutrition expert Jerry Brunetti to present an overview of the strategies and tools available for successful holistic herd health management. The emphasis is on natural alternatives for the treatment of common dairy cow problems, including complications in reproduction, birth and lactation. This video will provide you with a basic understanding of the power and the limitations of herbs, how to treat the whole cow, and how to build a herbal medicine kit for your farm. Drawing on actual case studies, which are examined, diagnosed, and treated using holistic protocols, this video serves as a virtual hands-on course in holistic herd health that will prove invaluable to every dairy producer, from the micro-scale family farmer to commercial-scale operations. *DVD format, 90 minutes. PAL format for Europe, Australia, etc.*

To order call 1-800-355-5313
or order online at www.acresusa.com

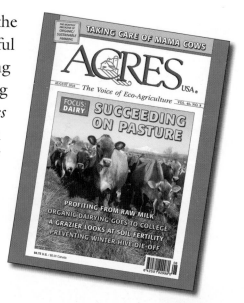